Productive Agriculture & A Quality Environment

OD PRODUCTION, LIVING, RECREATION
THE RURAL-URBAN INTERFACE

NATIONAL ACADEMY
OF SCIENCES

Productive Agriculture & A Quality Environment

FOOD PRODUCTION, LIVING, RECREATION
THE RURAL-URBAN INTERFACE

Committee on Agriculture and the Environment

DIVISION OF BIOLOGY AND AGRICULTURE

NATIONAL RESEARCH COUNCIL

NATIONAL ACADEMY OF SCIENCES

WASHINGTON, D.C.

1974

This study was supported by the U. S. Department of Agriculture.

Library of Congress Cataloging in Publication Data

National Research Council. Committee on Agriculture and the Environment.
    Productive agriculture & a quality environment.

    Bibliography: p.
    1. Agricultural ecology–United States. 2. Environmental policy–United States.
    3. Environmental protection–United States. 4. United States–Rural, conditions.
    I. Title.
S601.N35 1974   301.31'0973   74-6355
ISBN 0-309-02215-0

Available from

Printing and Publishing Office, National Academy of Sciences
2101 Constitution Avenue, N.W., Washington, D.C. 20418

Printed in the United States of America

Preface

The continuing interaction between Nature's resources and an increasing human population with its need for food and shelter demands technological periodic adjustment. In response to a request from the Secretary of Agriculture to the President of the National Academy of Sciences, this Committee has considered these interactions as they relate to agriculture and the environment. The Committee sought to identify and examine major facets that contribute either positively or negatively to the two main questions posed:

• What strategies can be used to maintain a strong food and fiber industry in this country, while eliminating or minimizing environmental conflicts resulting from production practices?
• What can be done to make rural America a more pleasing place to live?

One outcome of the Committee's work was the volume entitled *Degradation of Synthetic Organic Molecules in the Biosphere,* appearing in 1972. This report considers the persistence of chemicals in the soil, water or food chain after application in food production practice.

In selecting areas of major concern, several with obvious long-range critical impact were not specifically considered in depth. Among these

iii

are the management of public and privately owned forests, the availability and distribution of mobile fuels essential to present agricultural production, and the implications of technical breakthroughs not yet being applied. No special emphasis was given to the degree of American involvement in the production of the world food supply or to the impact of humanitarian or foreign exchange considerations.

The Committee wishes to express its appreciation to a number of persons who have contributed to the work. We have benefited greatly from the availability of Dr. Sidney L. Spahr, who during 18 months of leave from the University of Illinois, Urbana, served as a staff officer of the National Research Council in support of the Committee's work. Among his contributions are the editing of the report on chemical additives and the present full report of the Committee. Dr. Michael R. DeCarlo, Executive Secretary of the Agricultural Board, now retired, arranged numerous conferences with informed persons, secured needed documents, and supplied valuable encouragement, aid, and counsel. His replacement, Dr. Joyce Torio, has served effectively in many roles. We wish to express our debt and sincere appreciation to these and other excellent staff associates.

In addition to several specific acknowledgments made in the body of the text, we wish to thank the following persons for technical advice and counsel:

University of Illinois—D. L. Day, Professor of Agricultural Engineering, R. S. Englebrecht, Professor of Environmental Engineering, Raymond J. Miller, Professor of Soil and Physical Chemistry, G. W. Salisbury, Professor of Dairy Science; *Cornell University*—N. C. Brady; *Iowa State University* (Department of Economics)—S. H. Hargrove, E. O. Heady, H. C. Madson, and K. J. Nicol; *University of Minnesota*—H. O. Halvorson, Professor of Biochemistry and Microbiology; *University of Missouri*—J. C. Headley; *University of California* (Los Angeles)—James V. Clark, Professor of Organization and Development, J. D. MacKenzie, Professor of Engineering; *U.S. Department of Agriculture* (Washington, D.C.)—V. M. Davis, P. E. Schleusener, and William Whyte; *Washington, D.C.*—J. L. Buckley, *Office of Science and Technology;* Marion Clawson, *Resources for the Future;* H. P. Glascock, *American Society of Foresters;* W. K. Reilly and Lee M. Talbot, *Council on Environmental Quality. Environmental Protection Agency,* Ada, Oklahoma—William S. Galegar. *U.S. Department of the Interior,* Pittsburgh, Pennsylvania—C. Alex Mills. J. S. V. McAllister, Belfast, Northern Ireland; Olle Noren, Uppsala, Sweden; C. T. Riley, Ministry of Agriculture, Fisheries and Food, Surrey, England; R. Thaer, Vundsallee, West Germany.

Committee on Agriculture and the Environment

I. C. GUNSALUS (*Chairman*), Department of Biochemistry, University of Illinois, Urbana, Illinois

A. R. BERTRAND, Dean of Agricultural Sciences, Texas Tech University, Lubbock, Texas

ARNE E. CARLSON, E. I. du Pont de Nemours, Wilmington, Delaware

STANLEY DAGLEY, Department of Biochemistry, University of Minnesota, St. Paul, Minnesota

ALVIN C. DALE, Department of Agricultural Engineering, Purdue University, Lafayette, Indiana

HERRELL DEGRAFF, American Meat Institute, Chicago, Illinois

WENDELL W. KILGORE, Department of Environmental Toxicology, University of California, Davis, California

ROBERT W. MORISON, Science, Technology and Society, Cornell University, Ithaca, New York

DAVID PIMENTEL, Department of Entomology, Cornell University, Ithaca, New York

JOHN F. TIMMONS, Department of Economics, Iowa State University, Ames, Iowa

PAUL E. WAGGONER, Department of Soils and Climatology, Connecticut Agricultural Experiment Station, New Haven, Connecticut

ROBERT H. WHITE-STEVENS, Bureau of Conservation and Environmental Sciences, Rutgers University, New Brunswick, New Jersey

A. RICHARD WILLIAMS, Architect, Champaign, Illinois

SUBCOMMITTEES

Environmental Design

A. R. WILLIAMS (*Chairman*), University of Illinois
P. H. LEWIS, University of Wisconsin
R. L. KNOWLES, University of Southern California
R. B. RILEY, University of Illinois

Chemical Additives

W. W. KILGORE (*Chairman*), University of California, Davis
A. E. CARLSON, E. I. du Pont de Nemours
D. PIMENTEL, Cornell University
STANLEY DAGLEY, University of Minnesota

Plant and Animal By-products

A. C. DALE (*Chairman*), Purdue University
H. DEGRAFF, American Meat Institute
R. C. LOEHR, Cornell University

Resource Allocation

A. R. BERTRAND (*Chairman*), Texas Tech University
P. E. WAGGONER, Connecticut Agricultural Experiment Station
J. F. TIMMONS, Iowa State University
R. WHITE-STEVENS, Rutgers University
J. F. KENNEDY, University of Iowa

Contents

vii

1

Introduction

That continuous changes in population, developments in technology, and fluctuations in nature introduce stresses of variable intensity and time scale is well-recognized. That there is competition for resources and that differences exist over the mode of their application can be found in statements throughout history. What is new to the present age is the realization that, in some regions at least, the depletion of resources and the accumulation of products of human interaction have reached a critical point in terms of health, productivity and survival. This situation impinges on the production of essential food and shelter and thus, in large measure, involves agriculture.

In certain areas of concern, the sorting out and application of current knowledge can be expected to improve the interplay of production and expenditure of natural resources with the quality of the environment. In others, additional information and manpower—including facilities for education, research and application—may well be required to meet developing needs. Three general areas of concern were considered in this report: agricultural production capability and its by-products, maintenance and improvement of a pleasant rural environment, and competition in allocation and distribution of resources (i.e., the land, water, and energy essential for the agricultural, industrial, and recreational activities of the United States population.

Early in the deliberations, the Committee acknowledged that entre-
preneurial activities, and any changes therein, would be motivated primarily by economic gain. In contrast, public law, as distinct from private
(individual grievance) law, was seen as the predominant modulating or
directive force. Public law is expected to respond in this regard in a
corrective manner, rather than as a planning mechanism. To whatever
degree resource planning is to be a force, the greater potential lies in
a regional approach rather than in schemes based on political boundaries.
Agricultural resource survey and planning action can be said to have
taken the lead in terms of accumulated experience on a regional basis
and in cooperative interstate interaction. The Committee has not explored
in depth the economic and public law implications of planning and resource allocation, although these should certainly receive adequate attention by a qualified group. It is also obvious that many of the interactions
between economic gain and public regulation can be considered use-
fully only via a broader base than agriculture alone. Resource cost, allocation, and distribution are general environmental and population
problems. The individual producer in agriculture is at the mercy of
supply and demand. Industry, including agricultural industry, can outbid
the small producer for resources.

The degree to which the American public and its government sub-
scribe to the need for long-range planning is not clear. At the outset
of the study the latest published data were for 1960 or 1965. To the
extent possible, 1970 data were brought in later as a more definitive
base for extrapolation to 1980 and beyond. There is a clear need for
computer-based resource data banks including coefficients relative to
the cost in dollars and environmental insult of the several options for
agricultural production. The fraction of the United States export that
is currently derived from agricultural products emphasizes the growing need for accurate, up-to-date information. The forms in which
the resource inventories are stored, their distribution (availability),
and the means for updating and refining primary data are critical.
Care in how assumptions are stated and changes of method or base
are likewise critical.

Any extensive attempt to plan for the maintenance and enhancement
of the quality of rural America will most certainly be in competition,
if not open conflict, with the free-enterprise development of rural land
and utilization of water and energy. Historically, agriculture has not
been a highly profitable or rapidly changing enterprise. Little attention
has been given to the planning of rural power distribution or arteries of
transportation, or to selection of sites for residences, in accordance with
aesthetics and prudence. Rather, planners have been extravagant in

their use of the richest croplands. Most attempts to improve the rural environment have been too idealistic, or too little based on experience and verified data, or infeasible on economic and regulatory grounds. The economics imposed by multiple suppliers—and the time scale imposed by biological constraints on cropping practices, application of nutrients, and use of crop protection chemicals and equipment—permit wide fluctuations in supply and price structure. The shifts in procedures related to rearing of animals for meat, eggs and milk have been even slower than in crop production. In the absence of informed advice, these activities seem likely to continue to respond on a time scale that is ineffective and inappropriate. The further impact of increased energy utilization relative to supply in the United States, and of distribution problems that coincide with peak planting and harvest periods, will result in absolute, as well as relative, losses in production.

Initiation of interdisciplinary research and development on the topic of the environmental impact of agriculture, exploration of means to improve communication in rural areas, and enlargement of data sources are three steps toward resolution of some of the general problems that impinge most heavily on the economic viability and development of the agricultural industry.

Evaluations and recommendations are but part of an unending adjustment. In a few instances agricultural practice has posed problems for which the manpower and the method of solution are either economically infeasible or technically unsound. In some instances the immediate response mechanism may prove fruitful; in others it may generate even greater concern.

2

Recommendations

The Committee's recommendations are designed (1) to permit the continued production of food and fiber, while minimizing environmental conflicts, and (2) to improve rural America as a place in which to live. While most of the recommendations may be implemented through the United States Department of Agriculture (USDA), several involve policies of other governmental agencies. Where these latter situations exist, recommendations are phrased accordingly. Problems concerning environmental conflicts in food production and rural living are too interwoven with the total demands of society and the national economy to be solved by USDA alone.

Several areas merit immediate action in the form of changes in policy, increased research effort, or changes in priorities. These include improvement of nationwide systems to monitor pest populations, pest damage to crops, and the cost–benefit relationships of various methods of pest control; initiation of developmental research and its application at the farm level to odor control and waste disposal in livestock-production units; establishment of a national land-use program that considers land and water needs for food and fiber production, aesthetic quality of the rural landscape, urbanization of rural lands and the impact on the patterns of rural growth of siting public service facilities; and implementation of a major program for guiding growth and providing services in rural areas.

FOOD AND FIBER PRODUCTION

Food and fiber research has been generally successful in developing methods to produce abundant, high-quality food at low cost. Support for research and development of new methods for increasing the efficiency of food and fiber production should continue to have a high priority. The total effort should include a greater emphasis on environmental and societal demands, at the same time recognizing that the continued increase in yields *per se* (i.e., efficiency of food production) is a highly desirable national goal. Attributes of a policy to help meet overall societal demands include (1) freeing land for such uses as recreation, living space, parks and greenbelts; (2) minimizing the cost of food production; (3) continuing United States leadership in food production technology; and (4) providing goods for export.

Increased emphasis should be placed on developing a computer model of the effects of environmental damage and environmental constraints. Estimates of costs and benefits, expected changes in food and fiber supply and demand, recreational demand, and urbanization should be used to guide government policies on crop subsidies, exports, the use of natural resources, and the development of rural areas. Environmental questions bearing on land and water resource allocation policies for food and fiber production, for recreation and for improved quality of living should be thoroughly explored so that decisions will be based on the predictable results or on a range of alternatives. Changes in public attitudes, as they affect the demand for specific foods and use of natural resources, should be modeled and given increased attention in the establishment of government incentives and formulation of policies for food and fiber production, land use and water allocation. In areas where information is inadequate, it should be obtained through nationwide surveys or monitoring programs.

Crop-Protection Chemicals

The Committee believes that chemicals are necessary for the production of abundant, high-quality food and fiber; thus, the recommendations in this report are directed toward reducing the hazards involved in the use of crop-protection chemicals and reducing the quantities applied. The greatest opportunity for immediate reduction in the quantity of chemicals used to control agricultural pests, without reduction of their effectiveness, appears to lie in improving application techniques. To minimize problems associated with the application of crop-protection chemicals, the Committee recommends (1) that research on application techniques be intensified, and (2) that suitable regulations be established to restrict spray particle size to the largest compatible with effective pest control.

To foster the judicious use of crop protection chemicals, the Committee recommends that a program be established to monitor and forecast pest populations, thus enabling farmers to use chemicals on a "treat-when-necessary" basis. Although not necessarily feasible for every crop, the program could be applied to major crops, particularly in areas where there are extensive acreages of a single crop. It is also recommended that consideration be given to establishing a form of crop insurance for farmers when there are substantial risks of crop loss despite effective pest monitoring and forecasting.

The search for biodegradable crop-protection chemicals should be fostered by research in two areas: the use of model ecosystems, so that the capacity of a given chemical to concentrate in food chains can be determined in the laboratory; and the delineation of metabolic pathways employed by microbes to degrade natural products, so that the capabilities and limitations of the enzymes in completely oxidizing crop-protection chemicals may be accurately evaluated. Organic compounds may be changed into forms that are more persistent or more toxic or that accumulate in the food chain more rapidly than does the original compound. Disappearance, or lack of persistence, is not necessarily synonymous with degradation. Delineation of the metabolic pathways involved is necessary to ascertain that extensive degradation does indeed take place.

USDA should collect and maintain up-to-date records on crop losses and on the cost of pest control. These data should be used to assess the economic benefits resulting from the applications of crop-protection chemicals. Further, this information should be acquired by regions for the major crops. Information of this type is not readily available and, with but few exceptions, reliable determinations regarding the actual needs for crop-protection chemicals versus their economic benefits cannot now be made.

Recommendations for using crop-protection chemicals should be based on efficacy and on safety to the user and the environment. When more than one chemical is effective and economical for a particular pest problem, the chemical that is least hazardous to man and the environment should always be used. Increased emphasis on safety to man could lead to a significant reduction in the hazards associated with the application of crop-protection chemicals and post-spraying activities.

Guidelines should be established for the registration of new crop-protection chemicals. Under the present system, chemical companies frequently incur unnecessary expense and delay because they lack adequate guidelines. As a result, they are often forced to reduce their research on newer chemicals.

Wherever possible, crop rotation, sanitation, and other pest-reducing cultural practices should be encouraged. Increased use of these techniques could lead to a significant reduction in the need for chemicals.

Research should be intensified on alternative methods of pest control, especially in the areas of plant resistance and insect attractants. Emphasis in this area should be placed on those pests that (1) show promise of being controlled by an alternative method, (2) presently require large quantities of chemicals for their control, or (3) are a clear human health hazard. Obviously, the alternative method should be one posing lesser hazard to the environment.

A systems approach, utilizing interactions among land-use programs, crop-management practices, and production economics, is recommended for developing pest control programs. One aspect of this approach concerns the use of land now held out of production (under the land retirement program) to offset yield losses from insect damage that would occur in the event that the use of chemicals on specific crops is reduced by regulation. The Committee recommends that cost–benefit analyses be conducted to evaluate the feasibility of planting some or all of this land.

To foster the rational use of crop-protection chemicals, the Committee recommends that a program be established to evaluate the safety of produce that has minor blemishes or that contains insect parts. Current regulations aimed at elimination of insect parts on or in produce give rise to a situation wherein chemicals are used in abundance. Hence, careful cost–benefit evaluation is needed to assess "safety," "cosmetic appearance," and the acceptability of food commodities produced with a minimum of chemicals.

Chemical Fertilizer

Chemical fertilizer is essential to continued high yields of food and fiber at a relatively low cost. However, USDA should encourage the use of chemical fertilizer in a manner that will minimize nutrient enrichment of water. Procedures for minimizing leakage of plant nutrients into waterways should be ascertained and their implementation on agricultural land encouraged. Particular emphasis should be placed on minimizing leakage of the major eutrophication nutrients: phosphorus and nitrogen. Sources and modes of transport should be determined wherever nutrient enrichment is a problem.

The development of crop production practices that allow more efficient uptake of plant nutrients applied at high levels should be encouraged.

By-product Utilization

The Committee feels that the primary method for disposal of animal manures should be in the foreseeable future as it has been in the past, by recycling to the soil. The land has been and probably will remain an acceptable disposal point for treated and untreated animal waste under good crops and land management. Waste management practices require knowledge of the fate of organic and inorganic constituents in order to avoid (1) secondary pollution problems caused by runoff or percolation of soil water to groundwater or (2) an accumulation of salts sufficient to render the soil unfit for production. Additional investigations are needed to determine the capacity of the soil to assimilate waste, to delineate the degree of treatment that may be needed or applicable prior to land disposal, and to provide a better understanding of limitations on the capacity of land to accept waste.

Increased emphasis should be given to methods for the control of odors and the biochemistry of odor production. Animal-production units and urban housing are incompatible because the odors generated in the former are offensive. The technology of odor control is inadequate to provide effective and economically feasible solutions in most situations of high animal density.

Development and installation of complete farm-animal waste treatment and disposal systems should be accelerated and should utilize the findings of recent research. Demonstration projects should be used to speed the widespread adoption of successful approaches. Many such demonstration projects are needed for specific agricultural operations so that seasonal, geographic, management and size variations can be observed for information bearing on the feasibility and effectiveness of alternative waste management systems.

Innovative approaches to creating useful materials from animal manures and from other agricultural waste should receive greater research and development funds. Promising laboratory achievements should be field tested as quickly as possible.

The Committee recommends increased emphasis on education and training of personnel who have a prime interest in treating, utilizing, and disposing of agricultural by-products. Many of the scientists working on this problem, especially those outside of agricultural engineering, have been trained and have a primary interest in other areas, and their work on the disposal of agricultural by-products is secondary. Interdisciplinary effort should be encouraged by grants for training programs and research in

- biological sciences, especially microbiology, with prime interest in treating and utilizing by-products;
- agricultural and civil-sanitary engineering;
- animal sciences; and
- economics.

THE RURAL ENVIRONMENT

Quality of Rural Life

There is more to environmental quality than pollution abatement. Both the economic and social aspects of rural life must be improved if rural America is to be made a more desirable site for living. The Committee believes that qualitative aspects of the rural environment will become much more important as a basis for individual decisions on where to live than they have been in the past. Amenities and services available to rural areas must compare favorably with those available in urban areas. Society is likely to become increasingly service-oriented, more quality conscious, and less economically dependent upon proximity to an industrial urban center. If rural areas are in fact to be chosen as living sites, they must provide the services, amenities and qualities demanded by society.

A research and development program should be established to explore ways in which services can be improved in rural areas, especially those of low population. The provision of high level services would not only close the rural–urban gap but could attract people back to rural areas, offering a new economic base and relieving urban crowding. For example, such advances in remote communications and information-handling techniques as computer-based medical record-keeping, remote diagnosis, television and computer-based education—and good road systems—would permit people to settle in rural areas and small towns without having to concentrate near centralized medical facilities.

A substantial portion of federal funds spent on housing programs should be specifically allocated to rural housing. Such programs include loan guarantees (especially "low-risk"), rent subsidies, and public housing. Action-oriented research into problems peculiar to rural areas, utilization of rural building skills in self-help renovation projects, and the use of prefabricated utility cores and construction systems should receive additional financial support.

Amenities that attract people to rural areas should be identified through research. It should be determined where, and for what reasons, people tend to settle in rural areas when they are no longer economically bound to an industry-based city. An obvious example of persons in this category are those who retire after 20 or 30 years of government service—the investigation could well start with a study of their attitudes and choices.

Regions that have high existing or potential amenity value and where natural resources can support an increased population with little environmental conflict should be identified. They should be selectively supported as living locations. Such a selection of specific regions is desirable, rather than the mere provision of general incentives for more widespread population redistribution. By this means, people will be attracted into new areas and the desirable characteristics of regions that are less well-endowed with natural amenities will be preserved. Government support for such regions should include assistance with physical planning, provision of a portion of the economic base, provision of services, and protection and enhancement of existing natural amenities.

Special emphasis should be given to the encouragement of methods for controlling undesirable development in rural areas that should, instead, be preserved for their natural beauty, cultural significance or high inherent food productivity.

Physical Design of Rural Areas

Rural communities and small towns in the United States have developed primarily around economic patterns, with little attention to aesthetics and the preservation of natural amenities. Recommendations bearing on the design of rural areas assume that greater disposable income and changing social values will enhance the role of quality and aesthetics in the future selection of a living site for many people.

Rural development programs should increasingly emphasize aesthetics and quality, especially in areas where population growth is being stimulated. USDA should make further use of the design professions to contribute to this aspect of rural growth.

Interdisciplinary groups (which might be termed environmental process teams), consisting of a carefully balanced group of specialists in natural and physical sciences, behavioral sciences, environmental design, and computer simulation—working closely with one another in various states and key regions—should be established. These groups should coordinate research, education and decision-making that bear on environmental aspects of regional development and site selection for major service facilities. These teams should be joint local–state–national ventures, accommodating local interests as well as state and federal coordination.

A major program of prototype regions comparable in size and scope with the "model cities" program is recommended as an approach to improving the physical design of rural America and the quality of rural life. The program would (1) provide funds for comprehensive and detailed planning and for environmental design of prototype sites; (2) demonstrate alternative ways to improve service systems and aesthetic and cultural values in rural areas and to manage growth and change in a manner that minimizes environmental conflicts; (3) stimulate economic health and direct growth, where appropriate; and (4) provide systematic evaluation of the prototype region. Environmental prototypes would thus be used to test and improve the information evolving from the work of the environmental process teams.

New qualitative standards for the aesthetic values of rural communities should be developed. Since standards are determined in part by sensitive human experience, judgment will be most valid if subjected to review and approval by qualified boards or commissions. Planning standards now in effect in both urban and rural areas are largely statistical, qualitative, and based on minimum performance standards (code enforcement criteria, for example). Beyond these factual and legally supportable standards, new qualitative standards as measured against acknowledged centers of excellence are needed to achieve a higher quality of life. The "Guide Michelin Principle," an analogy based on well-known qualitative comparison standards in tourism, could be applied generally and comprehensively in setting higher goals for urban and rural development.

New structures, whether single or developed as entire settlements, should be designed to use natural sources of energy—such as sun, wind, and water—and to take into account orientation, relation to natural cover, and the like. In so doing, demand for power and other energy sources brought to the site will be minimized. The existing environment reflects man's insensitivity and wastefulness in his demands for energy.

The environment should be given greater emphasis in USDA educational programs. Better environmental education is the implicit common denominator of most of the recommendations in this report, affecting as it does the full educational spectrum, from preschool through postdoctoral studies and public education. It is the central, long-range approach to substantial progress in enhancing the natural, rural and urban environment.

RESOURCES

Resource Allocation and Management

The primary resources associated with the production of food and fiber and with living in rural areas are land and water. While large areas of land are being appropriated annually for nonagricultural purposes, land and water resources appear adequate to meet the demands of even the highest predicted United States population increases by the year 2000; that is, if the production of food and fiber is concentrated on the most productive land and if trends in increases in unit productivity continue. The greatest uncertainty relates to the foreign demand for United States-produced food, although population increase and changes in the public attitude toward specific foods could be important factors in determining total demand. Change in unit productivity, environmental constraints, productivity of land used for food and fiber production, and government subsidies for irrigation water, crop production and land retirement appear to be the most important factors determining total production.

There is an urgent need to devise and implement a national land-use policy. Inefficiencies and waste in the use and misuse of land and resources, both natural and human, are already enormous and are increasing. A comprehensive national effort is urgently needed to guide growth and change on a national scale and to support regional, state and local planning.

A centralized resource data bank should be established and maintained to provide a consistent and comprehensive source of information for planning. Such a data bank should include an inventory of natural and cultural resources with detail suitable and sufficient for computer simulation. Examples of data needed include topography, soil capability characteristics as developed by the Soil Conservation Service, drainage, rainfall, waterways, fragile environmental areas, mineral and energy resources, population distribution, service corridors, and accumulation of man-made structures with particular emphasis on areas of unique natural and cultural diversity.

First priority should be given to an inventory of those agricultural production areas at the urban–rural interface that are under heavy pressure from a growing population. The urban–rural interface should also have a high priority in setting up action programs. Continuous urbanization without regard to the surrounding area is one of the nation's most acute land-use conflicts. Growth should be controlled to minimize environmental conflicts at the growing edge, even though such controls generally run counter to the desires of the individual landowner. The policy should specifically protect lands at the urban fringe, encourage clustering of new community modules and services wherever the carrying capacity of the land permits, and encourage higher intensity redevelopment of inner city areas.

Action should be taken to preserve land for food and fiber production in those areas of the United States where soil characteristics and climate favor high yields and efficient production. Such land should be given high priority consideration in land-use planning, especially in those highly populated areas where there is competition for land between food and fiber production and urban or suburban development. To remove the most fertile land from crops will cause a disproportionate increase in food prices. Crops should be grown where energy requirements will be least, and urban development should be directed elsewhere.

USDA development and incentive programs should be designed to maximize the use of highly productive areas with favorable climates for food production. Except in areas strategically located or having unique production capabilities, development of arid or semiarid land for food production is questionable because of energy costs and competing demands for water. Allocation of energy and water to arid and semiarid areas for production of food and fiber should be made only when there are special societal requirements for the products. Water development projects requiring major expenditures in arid and semiarid lands should be multipurpose. Likewise, the development of marginally productive soils should not be encouraged. An extended effort should be made to produce food and fiber in areas where energy requirements can be minimized.

Fragile areas (areas that if used intensively or used for purposes at variance with natural characteristics would deteriorate rapidly or require excessive inputs to maintain the new use) should be identified and preserved. USDA should cease supporting actions that bring about major changes in the characteristics and use of fragile areas. Special reference is made here to wetlands, mountain woodlands, steep arid areas, and other areas of unusual aesthetic value. On a national scale, additional cropland is not now needed, and intensive use of fragile land would conflict with wildlife production, recreational uses and long-range environmental benefits to society. Retention of fragile land areas for less intensive uses will serve to enhance wildlife and recreation and as a form of land storage for possible future use in food production.

Innovative approaches should be sought by USDA to preserve land and water now available for outdoor recreation and to encourage strategic development of new public and private areas for outdoor recreation.

A national plan for meeting society's needs for outdoor recreation is critically essential.

USDA should accelerate research and action programs to minimize erosion of agricultural land and stream banks. Sediment in streams has three principal sources: new construction sites, agricultural land, and stream banks. Retention of sediment on agricultural land would increase water infiltration and reduce the quantities of agricultural pollutants reaching the waterways. Control of stream-bank erosion would minimize damage to land and facilities adjacent to streams and reduce the sediment load in the streams.

Increased emphasis should be placed on monitoring the impact of major land-use and hydrologic changes upon animal and plant communities. Lack of basic knowledge now limits our ability to predict the effect of human intervention on natural ecosystems. Studies should concentrate on projects where a good data base exists or can be obtained, where environmental impact studies anticipate major environmental change, and where collection and interpretation of data would be useful in predicting changes whenever similar ecosystems are disturbed.

Energy

The energy needs of society cannot be divorced from agricultural needs. In fact, the demand for energy in the form of electricity and fuel is one that must be met in rural areas if they are to be made attractive living sites. Agriculture is also concerned with siting facilities for producing energy. Such sites should be carefully selected to minimize environmental conflicts with land use and to avoid destroying sites of natural and cultural diversity. A third consideration relates to energy for agricultural production. Mobile fuels are a necessary part of agricultural technology today. In the event that availability of energy becomes a limiting factor in overall economic growth, high priority should be given to supplying mobile fuel for food and fiber production. Increased research emphasis should be placed on producing food in a manner that will minimize expenditure of energy.

FOOD AND FIBER PRODUCTION

3

Crop-Protection Chemicals

The survival of mankind depends upon the economical and abundant production of food. In modern agricultural practice, this objective is achieved by maintaining monocultures, permitting the maximum use of machinery from seedtime to harvest. It requires little imagination to appreciate the fact that such monocultures are not the product of nature: They were devised by man and are maintained only by the exercise of vigilance and the expenditure of considerable energy. Thus, Metcalf (1971) has compared a midwestern cornfield with its predecessor, the tall grass prairie. He pointed out that the cornfield ideally contains only a single species without any competitors (parasites or predators), whether bacterial, fungal, weed, nematode, insect, bird or rodent; whereas the prairie consisted of perhaps a hundred plant species and thousands of associated animals.

Crop monocultures are susceptible to pest outbreaks in part because of their simplicity and instability. An equally important cause of pest outbreaks in crops is that natural resistance has been inadvertently bred out of the plants, making the crops highly susceptible to pest attack. In the case of certain crops, pest outbreaks can be controlled effectively only by the use of pesticides. Were this practice to be discontinued, a few of the major crops characteristic of modern agriculture could not be maintained. Less efficient, alternative practices would call for additional manpower and expenditure of energy on a tremendous scale. It is necessary, therefore, to encourage public appreciation of the benefits conferred by the use of pesticides, appreciation that would balance present fears concerning the effects of pesticides on the environment. Catastrophic harvest failures have occurred repeatedly down the ages as a result of destruction of crops by insects, and famines have been caused by fungal diseases—for example, the famine that Ireland experienced as a result of the destruction of the potato crop by late blight. Disasters on this scale are now largely a thing of the past. But mounting antipathy toward the use of chemical pesticides may discourage the manufacture of beneficial products and the development of products to combat dangers that have not yet emerged.

Development of new pesticides involves very large investments in time and resources (Naegele, 1971), and not all the products are successful. In one case, development took 9 years from invention to the date of registration. The direct investment in that period was $6.4 million, and 1 year later (in 1970), the cumulative cash position was a negative $4.6 million. If, as an alternative, the money had been invested at 8 percent, the cash position 10 years after invention would have been a positive $6.1 million. However, the manufacturer estimated that profits from this product would ultimately justify the investments if the product were not replaced in a few years by a better one (Naegele, 1971). He also stated that, even with a great technical success, a manufacturer of agricultural chemicals has few opportunities to realize a profit on an investment of $10 million in research and $3–10 million in plant facilities.

Chemical additives have been used for hundreds of years to increase crop yields, but the discovery in 1867 that Paris green could control the Colorado beetle probably marked the beginning of the use of commercial pesticides. The discovery undoubtedly led to the commercial use of calcium and lead arsenate, well-known pesticides of the late 1800's and early 1900's. Today almost 900 chemical pesticides are available for the protection of crops, agricultural produce, and processed and stored foods (U.S. Department of HEW, 1969).

The use of pesticides in agriculture has permitted the farmer to produce some foods at a lower cost and thus has reduced the cost of food and fiber products for the consumer. In addition, along with other technological advances in agriculture, pesticides have served to increase the capability of the individual farmer. It is estimated that at the present time one farmer produces food and fiber for 46 persons, whereas in 1850 he produced only enough for 4 persons and in 1960 enough for 25 persons (Metcalf, 1971).

A marked increase in the development and use of pesticides occurred in the late 1940's and extended into the 1950's and 1960's. According to the United States Tariff Commission (USDA, 1971d), the production and sale of synthetic organic pesticides increased steadily from 1940 until 1968. During the 5-year period 1964–1968, the average annual increase in the sale of pesticides was 8 percent. In 1969, however, this trend was broken when the volume of producers' sales dropped to 3.2 percent below those in 1968. Table 1 shows both the production and sales figures of synthetic organic pesticides in the United States from 1960 to 1969.

Historically, pesticides have been categorized according to their use, even though some overlap does occur in each of the classes. The major categories are insecticides, herbicides, fungicides, rodenticides, and fumigants. Collectively, these pesticides account for more than 90 percent of all pesticides sold (USDA, 1971d). Some of the more popular pesticides are listed in Table 2.

TABLE 1 Synthetic Organic Pesticides: Production and Sales, United States, 1960–1969[a]

Year	Quantity (1,000 lb)	Increase over Previous Year (%)	Value ($1,000)	Increase over Previous Year (%)
Production[b]				
1960	647,795	10.6	307,293	14.4
1961	699,699	8.0	361,983	17.8
1962	729,718	4.3	427,373	18.1
1963	763,477	4.6	456,068	6.7
1964	782,749	2.5	481,955	5.7
1965	877,197	12.1	582,899	20.9
1966	1,013,110	15.5	727,772	24.9
1967	1,049,663	3.6	963,639	32.4
1968	1,192,360	13.6	1,066,775	7.0
1969[c]	1,104,381	−7.4	1,052,129	−1.4
Sales (Domestic and Export)				
1960	570,397	13.4	261,789	16.1
1961	611,917	7.3	302,955	15.7
1962	633,962	3.6	346,301	14.3
1963	651,471	2.8	369,140	6.6
1964	692,355	6.3	427,111	15.7
1965	763,905	10.3	497,066	16.4
1966	822,256	7.6	583,802	17.4
1967	897,363	9.1	787,043	34.8
1968	959,631	6.9	849,240	7.9
1969[c]	928,663	−3.2	851,166	0.2

SOURCE: Table 1, *The Pesticide Review 1970* (USDA, 1971d), p. 6.
[a] Includes a small quantity of soil conditioners.
[b] Values calculated from production and unit sales value, manufacturers' level.
[c] Preliminary.

TABLE 2 Pesticidal Chemicals: Production by Classes, United States, 1966-1969

Pesticides	Quantity (1,000 lb)			
	1966	1967	1968	1969[a]
Fungicides				
Copper naphthenate	3,211	3,473	1,718	1,545
Copper sulfate[b]	41,504	33,992	37,192	42,072
Ferbam	1,379	2,331	1,900	1,500[c]
Mercury fungicides	1,035	912	1,448[d]	941
Nabam	2,053	1,361	2,000[c]	1,938
Pentachlorophenol (PCP)[e]	43,262	44,239	48,575	45,988
2,4,5-Trichlorophenol and salts[d]	17,929	25,254	28,066	f
Zineb	4,721	3,055	3,081	2,500[c]
Other organic fungicides	63,816	63,269	66,793	85,607
Total[g]	178,910	177,886	190,773	182,091
Herbicides				
2,4-D acid[h]	(68,182)	(77,139)	(79,263)	(47,077)
2,4-D acid esters and salts	72,522	83,750	94,116	56,998
DNBP, ammonium salt	85	58	f	f
Phenyl mercuric acetate (PMA)[i]	502	518	582	534
Sodium chlorate[j]	32,000	30,000	30,000	30,000
2,4,5-T acid[h]	(15,489)	(14,552)	(17,530)	(4,999)
2,4,5-T acid esters and salts	18,059	27,189	42,542	11,626
Other organic herbicides	148,853	206,759	235,541	272,606
Total	272,021	348,274	402,781	371,764
Insecticides, Fumigants, Rodenticides[k]				
Aldrin-toxaphene group[l]	130,470	120,183	115,974	107,311
Calcium arsenate	2,890	2,008	3,398[d]	2,000[c]
DDT	141,349	103,411	139,401	123,103
Dibromochloropropane	8,722	5,240	7,887	8,611
Lead arsenate	7,328	5,952	9,016[d]	7,000[c]
Methyl bromide[m]	16,345	19,665	20,454	20,033
Methyl parathion	35,862	33,344	38,163	50,572
Parathion	19,444	11,361	20,000[c]	f
Other organic insecticides	199,820	202,600	227,326	260,892
Total	562,230	503,764	581,619[d]	579,522
GRAND TOTAL	1,013,161	1,029,924	1,175,173	1,133,377

SOURCE: Table 2, *The Pesticide Review 1970* (USDA, 1971d), p. 7.
[a] Preliminary.
[b] Shipments by producers to agriculture (including for use a minor plant nutrient).
[c] Estimated.
[d] Revised.
[e] Not only a wood preservative for wood rot control but a herbicide and desiccant.
[f] Separate figure not available.
[g] Sulfur not included; may amount to 150 million pounds.
[h] Figures in parentheses, because of duplication, are not included in totals.

The overall use patterns of pesticides have changed considerably; for instance, the use of herbicides in the United States has grown rapidly during recent years. Herbicides have become an important factor in modern farming because they have replaced farm labor, and in some cases are much more efficient than mechanical methods. Because of these and other factors, herbicide production grew at the rate of 22 percent a year during the five years prior to 1969, compared with 8 percent for all pesticides. In 1969 synthetic organic herbicides accounted for 36 percent of all pesticides produced in the United States. Their sales exceeded insecticides for the first time in 1967; the lead has continued to increase since then. They represented 58 percent of all pesticide dollar sales in 1969, whereas insecticides, fumigants, rodenticides, and certain other chemicals captured 34.6 percent of the pesticide market (Table 3). On the other hand, herbicides represented only 33.5 percent of the total pounds of pesticides sold, while insecticides accounted for 53.1 percent (Table 3).

According to USDA reports, 85 percent of all farmers used pesticides in 1966, and, of those used, over 90 percent were applied to crops (USDA reports 147 and 179, 1968a, and 1970e, respectively). The remaining 10 percent was shared about equally between livestock and various uses around the farm. American farmers, of course, do not use all the pesticides manufactured by United States producers. Of the total poundage produced in the United States, 38 percent is used by agriculture, 25 percent is exported, 25 percent is purchased by governmental, industrial and institutional organizations, and 12 percent is sold on the domestic market (*Chemical Week,* 1963).

In agriculture, pesticides are applied principally to cotton and corn. Almost half, 47 percent, of the insecticides used on crops in 1966 were used on cotton and 17 percent on corn (Table 4). Also, in 1966, herbicides were applied mainly to corn (41 percent of all herbicides used, Table 5). Weed control in cotton fields was maintained, however, by using only 6 percent of herbicides sold. Thus, 64 percent of the insecticides and 47 percent of the herbicides marketed in 1966 were used on just two crops, cotton and corn. Collectively, then, 46.3 percent of all pesticidal chemicals used by farmers in 1966 was applied to these two

---

i Also a fungicide.

j Estimated shipments to producers of herbicides and defoliants.

k Includes a small quantity of synthetic soil conditioners; does not include the fumigants carbon tetrachloride, carbon disulfide, ethylene dibromide, and ethylene dichloride, which have many other uses; nor does it include paradichlorobenzene (classed by the Tariff Commission as an intermediate) or inorganic rodenticides.

l Includes aldrin, chlordane, dieldrin, endrin, heptachlor, Strobane, and toxaphene.

m Fumigant for control of both insects and weeds.

TABLE 3 Synthetic Organic Pesticides: Volume and Value of Sales by Classes, United States, 1967–1969[a]

Class	1967		1968		1969[b]	
	Amount	% of Total	Amount	% of Total	Amount	% of Total
Volume of Sales (1,000 lb)						
Fungicides	120,413	13.4	129,961	13.5	124,418	13.4
Herbicides and plant hormones	287,582	32.1	318,554	33.2	311,157	33.5
Insecticides, fumigants, rodenticides, and soil conditioners[c]	489,368	54.5	511,116	53.3	493,088	53.1
TOTAL	897,363	100.0	959,631	100.0	928,663	100.0
Value of Sales ($1,000)						
Fungicides	56,333	7.2	62,061	7.3	61,174	7.2
Herbicides and plant hormones	429,980	54.6	483,330	56.9	495,670	58.2
Insecticides, fumigants, rodenticides, and soil conditioners[c]	300,730	38.2	303,849	35.8	294,322	34.6
TOTAL	787,043	100.0	849,240	100.0	851,166	100.0

SOURCE: Table 3, *The Pesticide Review 1970* (USDA, 1971d), p. 8.

[a] Classified by the Tariff Commission according to the most important use; many chemicals actually have uses in more than one major class; the herbicides involve some repetition (see Table 2).

[b] Preliminary.

[c] A grouping required by the Tariff Commission to meet its need for separate data on cyclic chemicals; fumigants included may be fungicidal, nematocidal, and/or herbicidal as well as insecticidal.

crops. Although complete data are not yet available, it now appears that the use of pesticides on soybeans has increased steadily since 1966.

Concern for the health of the public consuming foods containing pesticide residues emerged during the late 1940's, and tolerances were established in 1954 for pesticides on raw agricultural commodities, as regulated by the Federal Food Drug and Cosmetic Act and amended by the Miller Bill of 1954 (Public Law 518). This legislation limited the quantity of pesticide residues allowed in or on fruits, vegetables, and other agricultural products. Thus, human health became an important factor in assessing the risks and benefits of pest control recommendations. In the 1960's public interest was focused on the deterioration of the environment caused by pesticides, and federal legislation establishing the Environmental Protection Agency followed in an effort to institute protection of the environment from all pollutants.

Clearly, from now on, all control programs employing pesticides or bioenvironmental measures will continue to be assessed by the public on the basis of three important criteria—economics, public health, and environmental pollution. A serious deficiency in any one of these criteria could easily prevent a pest control technique from being used.

Many overviews of the interactions between crop-protection chemicals and the environment are available. The reader is especially referred to publications by the American Chemical Society (1969) and Wadleigh (1968), the report prepared by a joint task force of USDA and the Directors of Land Grant Universities (USDA and the State Universities and Land Grant Colleges, 1968), the National Academy of Sciences publications *Weed Control*, Publ. 1597 (NAS, 1968b), and *Insect Pest Management and Control*, Publ. 1696 (NAS, 1969b), a report by the U.S. Department of HEW (1969), and the sections of the President's

TABLE 4   Farm Use of Insecticides by Crops, United States, 1964 and 1966[a]

Crop	Insecticide Use, 1964		Insecticide Use, 1966	
	Amount per Crop[b] (1,000,000 lb)	% of Total	Amount per Crop[b] (1,000,000 lb)	% of Total
Cotton	78.0	54	64.9	47
Corn	15.7	11	23.6	17
Vegetables[c]	9.7	7	11.1	8
Other field crops[d]	10.1	7	8.7	6
Apples	10.8	8	8.5	6
Fruits (not including apples and citrus)	4.5	3	6.6	5
Hay and pasture[e]	2.5	2	4.1	3
Tobacco	5.5	4	3.8	3
Soybeans	5.0	3	3.2	2
Citrus	1.4	1	2.9	2
Other	f	g	0.2	g
TOTAL (all crops)	143.2	100	137.6	100

SOURCE: *Quantities of Pesticides Used by Farmers in 1966* (USDA, 1970e).
[a] Does not include Alaska and Hawaii.
[b] Active ingredients; does not include petroleum.
[c] Includes potatoes as well as other vegetables.
[d] Includes wheat, sorghum, rice, peanuts, and sugarbeets, as well as other grains and other field crops.
[e] Includes alfalfa, other hay and forage, and pasture and rangeland.
[f] Less than 50,000 pounds.
[g] Less than 0.5 percent.

TABLE 5   Farm Use of Herbicides, by Crops, United States, 1964 and 1966[a]

	Herbicide Use, 1964		Herbicide Use, 1966	
Crop	Amount per Crop[b] (1,000,000 lb)	% of Total	Amount per Crop[b] (1,000,000 lb)	% of Total
Corn	25.5	33	46.0	41
Other field crops[c]	19.0[d]	25[d]	10.8	10
Pasture and rangeland	4.7	6	10.5	9
Soybeans	4.2	6	10.4	9
Wheat	9.2	12	8.2	7
Cotton	4.6	6	6.5	6
Vegetables[e]	4.8	6	5.7	5
Sorghum	2.0	3	4.0	4
Fruits and nuts[f]	1.0	1	3.6	3
Peanuts	[g]	[g]	2.9	3
Rice	[g]	[g]	2.8	2
Summer fallow	1.3	2	0.9	1
Nursery and greenhouse	[h]	[i]	0.1	[i]
TOTAL (all crops)	76.3	100	112.4	100

SOURCE: *Quantities of Pesticides Used by Farmers in 1966* (USDA, 1970e).
[a] Does not include Alaska and Hawaii.
[b] Active ingredients; does not include petroleum.
[c] Includes tobacco, sugarbeets, alfalfa, and other hay, as well as other grains and other field crops.
[d] Includes peanuts and rice in addition to the other field crops.
[e] Includes potatoes as well as other vegetables.
[f] Includes apples and citrus as well as other deciduous fruit and other fruit and nut crops.
[g] Included in other field crops.
[h] Less than 50,000 pounds.
[i] Less than 0.5 percent.

Science Advisory Committee report dealing with pesticides (Pimentel *et al.*, 1965a).

USE–BENEFIT ESTIMATE

USDA estimates (1965) on crop losses due to pests show a total loss of $9.9 billion, or 33.6 percent (Table 6). Losses due to insects and plants diseases have increased since the 1942–1951 period whereas losses from weeds have decreased significantly.

Use of synthetic insecticides has grown markedly since their introduction in 1946. Although crop losses due to insects have increased despite the significant use of insecticides, important advances have been made in reducing insect losses from certain pests. For example, reports indicate that losses from potato insects have declined from 22 percent in 1910–

TABLE 6 Comparison of Annual Losses in Agriculture for the Periods 1904, 1910–1935, 1942–1951, and 1951–1960, and an Estimate of Losses if No Pesticides Were Used

Years	Insects Loss, $[a]	Insects % of Total	Crop Diseases Loss, $[a]	Crop Diseases % of Total	Weeds Loss, $[a]	Weeds % of Total	Total for Period Loss, $[a]	Total for Period % of Loss, for All Periods	Potential Production, $[a]
No pesticide (based on 1960 data)	4.8[b]	16.3[b]	4.2[c]	14.2[c]	3.0[d]	10.2[d]	12.0	40.7	29.5[e]
1951–1960[f]	3.8	12.9	3.6	12.2	2.5	8.5	9.9	33.6	29.5[e]
1942–1951[g]	1.9	7.1	2.8	10.5	3.7	13.8	8.4	31.4	26.7
1910–1935[h]	0.6	10.5	NA[i]	NA	NA	NA	NA	NA	5.7[j]
1904[k]	0.4	9.8	NA	NA	NA	NA	NA	NA	4.1

SOURCE: Pimentel, D., "Extent of Pesticide Use, Food Supply, and Pollution," *Journal of the New York Entomological Society* 81: 13–33 (1973).

[a] Billion dollars.
[b] Assumes that, in addition to total crop losses of $3.8 billion on both treated and untreated acres due to insect attack (1951–1960 data), a $1.0 billion loss (Pimentel, 1972) would occur if 5 percent of the crop acres receiving insecticide treatment (USDA, 1968a) were left untreated.
[c] Assumes that, in addition to total crop losses of $3.6 billion on both treated and untreated acres due to crop disease (1951–1960) data, a $0.6 billion loss (Pimentel, 1972) would occur if the 0.5 percent of the crop acres receiving fungicide treatment (USDA, 1968a) were left untreated.
[d] Assumes that, in addition to the $2.5 billion loss (1951–1960) data due to weeds, the 12 percent of the acres receiving herbicides (USDA, 1968a) would require $0.5 billion (Pimentel, 1972) in cultivation and other weed control practices to provide equally effective crop production.
[e] Pest Losses (for 1960) + Actual Crop Production [for 1960 (USDA, 1961)] = Potential Crop Production. $9.9 billion + $19.6 billion = $29.5 billion.
[f] (USDA, 1965).
[g] (USDA, 1954).
[h] (Hyslop, 1938).
[i] Not available.
[j] Insect losses and crop production estimates for 1935 (USDA, 1936).
[k] (Marlatt, 1904).

25

1935 (Hyslop, 1938), to 16 percent in 1942–1951 (USDA, 1954), and to 14 percent in 1951–1960 (USDA, 1965). These reductions in crop loss might be expected, considering the effectiveness of insecticides for control of some major potato insect pests. The mean yield in bushels per untreated acre (without pesticides) was 283, compared with 312 on the treated acres—as high as 337 bushels in some regions (Post et al., 1949).

According to USDA estimates, however, corn losses due to insects have been increasing. A 3.5 percent loss was reported for the period 1942–1951 (USDA, 1954) and a 12.0 percent loss for the period 1951–1960 (USDA, 1965). Factors contributing to increased corn losses due to insects are the continuous culture of corn on the same land and the planting of insect-susceptible types (Metcalf et al., 1962; Bennett et al., 1967; Starks and McMillian, 1967).

Pimentel (1972) estimated that, without pesticides, crop losses due to insects would increase to $4.8 billion (16.3%), those due to diseases to $4.2 billion (14.2%), and those due to weeds to $3 billion (10.2%) (see Table 6). Total losses without pesticides is estimated at $12 billion, or 40.7 percent of potential crop production, an increased loss of 7.1 percent.

These estimated crop losses exaggerate the situation because insect, disease, and weed losses were measured separately and then added. For example, insect and disease attacks on apples were counted once as a loss for insects and once for disease. This approach led to an estimated total loss for apples from insects, diseases, and weeds of 150 percent (insects 60% + diseases 80%, weeds 10% = 150%). Obviously, total apple losses cannot be greater than 100 percent, and a more accurate estimate of loss in the absence of pesticides would be 90 percent. Recognizing that these loss figures, when added together, are exaggerated, an estimate of the costs and benefits of the use of pesticides can still be made.

The estimated increased annual dollar loss, if no pesticides were to be used, is $2.1 billion ($12.0 billion − $9.9 billion = $2.1 billion) (Table 6).

SIDE EFFECTS

Man

Pesticide residues in foods are a matter of concern to the consumer. This is due, at least in part, to articles appearing in the popular press that frequently magnify the significance of trace amounts of pesticide residues in foods and various other agricultural products. In a recent study conducted by Corneliussen (1970), it was found that pesticide residue levels detected in ready-to-eat foods remained at low levels during a 5-year Food and Drug Administration survey. From comparable data collected by the Food and Drug Administration between June 1964 and April 1968, the average daily pesticide intake from the diet was calculated and determined to be consistently low (Duggan and Weatherwax, 1967; Duggan and Lipscomb, 1969). In these studies, the residues of pesticide chemicals present in a high consumption, well-balanced diet were below—in most cases, substantially below—the limits established for acceptable daily intakes by the Food and Agriculture Organization and the World Health Organization (FAO/WHO, 1967). Also, there were no cases of levels above those anticipated when legal tolerances were initially established for food. In Corneliussen's study, food samples were analyzed for chlorinated hydrocarbons, organophosphates, chlorophenoxy acids, bromides, arsenic, amitrole, carbaryl (sevin), cadmium, and dithiocarbamate residues.

It thus appears that the small amounts of pesticide residues consumed by man in his daily diet do not constitute an immediate threat to his health. On the other hand, extensive studies have been conducted on tissue samples taken during surgery and in autopsies, and the results indicate that certain pesticides, particularly chlorinated hydrocarbons, do accumulate in selected body tissues (U.S. Department of HEW, 1969; Deichmann and MacDonald, 1971). Most of these and other studies have been focused on DDT and related chemicals primarily because they are considered persistent and because they accumulate in the food chain (Johnson *et al.*, 1971). The data have also been used to establish the amount of DDT and DDE present in the adipose tissue of the average United States citizen. It has not been established, however, that these chemicals pose any threat to health.

It is difficult to assess the long-term effects of low levels of pesticides and other similar chemicals that accumulate in human tissues. On the one hand, data presently available do not indicate that man is being harmed by small quantities of pesticides in his tissues; on the other hand, there are even fewer data to justify complacency. Since it is virtually impossible to live in an environment without chemicals, monitoring of chemical residues in body tissues and periodical reviews of the data should be continued indefinitely.

Probably the most important side effect on man resulting from the use of pesticides is occupational disease. The California Department of Public Health has been summarizing the acute affects of pesticides and other agricultural chemicals on California workers, as reported by physicians under the State's Workmen's Compensation system, since 1950. From these data the California Department of Public Health feels that "occupational disease caused by pesticides and other agricultural chemicals is one of the most important occupational health problems in the State." This is clearly stated in their summary of 1968 data, which is quoted in its entirety below.

SUMMARY OF 1968 DATA*

In 1968, there were 834 reports of occupational disease attributed to pesticides and other agricultural chemicals, 9 percent fewer than in 1967. Not included in the totals are about 500 reports of eye conditions and chemical burns which were reviewed but not tabulated this year.

The rate of occupational disease reports attributed to agricultural chemicals among agricultural service workers (5.7 per 1,000 service workers) was well over twice the rate for all workers in agriculture (2.1 reports per 1,000 agricultural workers). Structural pest control operators had a rate of 4.3 reports per 1,000 workers.

Since 1951, there have been 155 accidental deaths in California implicating agricultural chemicals: 34 of these were occupational incurred; 87 were of children and 34 were of adults in a nonwork situation. During 1968, there were no occupational deaths recorded, only the third year in this 18 year span free of such deaths.

Organic phosphate pesticides were responsible for 34 percent of the 834 cases; followed by herbicides, 8 percent, halogenated hydrocarbon pesticides, 8 percent, and fertilizers, 6 percent.

There were 216 reports of systemic poisoning in 1968. Organic phosphate compounds were blamed in 78 percent of these.

Farm laborers accounted for 52 percent of the 834 reports of occupational disease attributed to agricultural chemicals; other laborers, 15 percent; and operatives, including truck and tractor drivers, 14 percent. Farm laborers in this series were expected to be disabled for work more frequently than other occupations.

Occupational diseases are not included from among self-employed farmers and unpaid family labor, about one-fourth of the agricultural work force. Certain limitations of the occupational disease reporting system as they bear on the reported incidence of pesticide related illness are discussed.

Also, for the first 6-month period of 1969, some 420 poison control centers throughout the United States reported 2,163 poisoning cases attributed to insecticides, rodenticides, fungicides, and herbicides (FDA, 1970). Of the total pesticide cases reported, there were 14 fatalities. The report states further that the figures do not represent the total poisoning cases in the United States for the period covered because many cases are advised or treated, or both, by private physicians or hospitals that for the most part do not make reports to the centers.

The increasing use of parathion and other organophosphorus pesticides as substitutes for DDT and other chlorinated hydrocarbons has pre-

*Occupational Disease in California Attributed to Pesticides and Other Agricultural Chemicals, 1968. State of California, Department of Public Health, Bureau of Occupational Health and Environmental Epidemiology.

sented to the agricultural industry a new dimension of occupational hazards. In 1970, 1,172,491 pounds of parathion were used in California alone, putting it among the top chemical pesticides in terms of quantities used, and far ahead of any other organophosphate. Methyl parathion, a homolog, is of similar toxicity and is also used in large quantities (930,241 pounds in 1970). A rapid increase in the use of parathion was reflected in the fact that three times as much was used in Fresno County in 1970 as during a comparable period in 1968 (Unpublished data, Department of Environmental Toxicology, University of California, Davis).

Parathion is a highly toxic organophosphate insecticide. Its oral LD_{50} in rats is of the order of 5–10 mg/kg, and its mode of action is fairly well understood; i.e., oxidation to paraoxon and inhibition of cholinesterase. Thus, it is a neurotoxin, or nerve poison. Although a certain amount of information is available on parathion residues in plants and soils, relatively little is known about the levels at which such residues pose a health hazard for people who work in fields that have been treated with the pesticide. Parathion is readily absorbed through the skin and exerts its toxic action on contact with the skin or the eyes, or upon inhalation.

Until recently it was thought that parathion, when applied in the field, degraded within a few days to nontoxic substances. Recent studies indicate that parathion is stable and does not always degrade as had been believed (Kilgore *et al.*, 1972). After application, about 15 percent of the applied parathion is absorbed and translocated to most if not all internal components of the plants. The larger portion (85 percent) is volatilized as parathion and no metabolic or degradation products have been detected. In addition, parathion residues have been detected in grapevines 15 months after application.

Thus, because it is increasingly used and because it may persist in the environment, it is not surprising that parathion poisonings are being reported with increasing frequency in California and throughout the nation. These poisonings may be attributed, in part, to a lack of information—and even misinformation—about the fate of parathion after it is released into the environment.

Nontarget Organisms

Pesticides are powerful, essential control agents. Balanced against this is the vulnerable status of the life system, consisting of an estimated 200,000 species of plants and animals in the United States, of which man is a functioning part.

Man depends upon a variety of species for the maintenance of a quality atmosphere, for an adequate food supply, and for the biological degradation of wastes. In the presence of sunlight, plants take in carbon dioxide and water and release oxygen. The oxygen exists both as oxygen and ozone, which screens out lethal ultraviolet rays from the earth's surface. In addition, the plants are food for many animals in the food chain. Eventually, microorganisms release elements for reuse by plants. Nontarget species can serve another important role as a warning system for the dangerous effects of chemicals released into the environment.

The ecological impact of pesticides on the life system is a major concern (Pimentel, 1971). Most of the nearly one billion pounds of pesticides applied in 1970 was aimed at about 2,000 pest species; these make up only about 1 percent of the total of all species in the United States. As is to be expected, certain nontarget species were indirectly affected by the pesticides applied.

The effects upon nontarget species are diverse and often unpredictable. For example, DDE (a metabolite of DDT) is nontoxic to insects but is toxic to birds. Both DDE and DDT have brought about eggshell thinning (some 10–30%) in falcons, pelicans, and eagles; this has resulted in a decline in numbers the past few years of some predaceous bird populations (Keith, 1966; Hickey and Anderson, 1968; Fyfe et al., 1969; Porter and Wiemeyer, 1969; Wiemeyer and Porter, 1970; Keith, Wood and Hunt, 1970). DDE may also cause embryo mortality in mallards when it occurs at 40 ppm in their food (Heath et al., 1969).

Although the use of DDT and several of the other chlorinated insecticides in agriculture has declined significantly during the past few years, there is more information on the direct and indirect effects of DDT on nontarget species than on any other pesticides. Hence the ecological effects of DDT are presented here as examples of the diversity of the impact pesticides may have on the environment.

Predators at the top of the food chain are more often affected by pesticides than are animals lower in the food chain. An example of a species at the top of its food chain that was seriously reduced by a pesticide (DDT) is the lake trout in the Northeast. Trout reproduction ceased when the concentration of DDT in the eggs reached 5 ppm (Burdick et al., 1964). Trout eggs with this concentration hatched, but the young fry were killed as they utilized the last of the egg yolk containing DDT.

Insecticides have destroyed some beneficial natural enemies of insects in certain regions. When this situation occurred, pest population numbers exploded, causing serious damage to the crop (Lord, 1956; Paradis, 1956; Pimentel, 1961; Helle, 1965).

Reducing the numbers of one species may have indirect detrimental effects upon another. For example, when 2,4-D caused an 83 percent reduction in the forbs in a gopher habitat, an 87 percent reduction occurred in the gopher population itself (Keith *et al.*, 1959). DDT and other insecticides that have found their way into streams sometimes significantly reduce invertebrate populations on which trout and other fish depend (Hoffman *et al.*, 1946; Ide, 1957; Bridges and Andrews, 1961). In some cases, from 2–4 years were required for the streams to be repopulated with the same fauna.

Insecticides have been found to alter the normal behavior of some animals. For example, trout exposed to sublethal doses of DDT were found to lose their learned avoidance response (Anderson and Peterson, 1969), and mosquito fish preferred waters with higher levels of salinity than normal (Hansen, 1969). 2,4-D also caused predaceous coccinellid beetles to be sluggish (Adams and Drew, 1965). Sublethal dosages of dieldrin significantly affected the relearning ability of sheep (Van Gelder *et al.*, 1969).

Pesticides have been found to suppress growth in some species but to stimulate growth in others. White-tailed does, for example, when fed 5 ppm of dieldrin in their diet, grew more slowly than normal (Korschgen and Murphy, 1969). 2,4-D suppressed the growth of predaceous coccinellid beetle larvae (Adams, 1960), but stimulated the growth of the rice stem borer (Ishii and Hirano, 1963).

Pesticides have caused measurable changes in the reproduction of various nontarget species. White-tailed does fed 25 ppm of dieldrin in their diet, for example, had lower fawn survival than did untreated does (Korschgen and Murphy, 1969). In some natural habitats the brown pelican exposed to DDT and DDE has sufficiently high egg breakage to have resulted in complete reproductive failure (Keith *et al.*, 1970). Female mosquito fish reproduction was affected because they aborted their young after surviving exposure to sublethal dosages of toxaphene, DDT, DDE, methoxychlor, aldrin, endrin, heptachlor, and lindane (Boyd, 1964).

Certain pesticides may also increase the rate of reproduction in some organisms. For example the exposure of bean plants to 2,4-D increased aphid progeny production during a 10-day period from 139 to 764 per aphid mother (Maxwell and Harwood, 1960).

The chemical makeup of plants may be altered by pesticides, and this in turn affects the dependent nontarget species. Zinc, for example, was significantly higher (89 ppm dry weight) in bean plants exposed to heptachlor in the soil at 100 ppm than in unexposed bean plants (55 ppm); however, nitrogen levels were significantly lower (4.99 percent) in the exposed plants than in the unexposed controls (7.25 percent) (Cole *et al.*, 1968). Investigations have shown an increased protein content in wheat exposed to 2,4-D (Helgeson, 1947), in contrast with beans grown on 2,4-D-treated soil, which showed reduced protein content (Anderson and Baker, 1950).

Other important changes have been observed in plants after treatment with some herbicides. An example is the potassium nitrate level in sugar beets, which normally is less than 0.22 percent. When treated with sublethal concentrations of 2,4-D, the level increased to 4.5 percent, a level highly toxic to some animal species (Stahler and Whithead, 1950). In addition, the hydrocyanic acid content of Sudan grass was observed to increase 69 percent after treatment with 2,4,5-T (Swanson and Shaw, 1954).

In nature many different kinds of organisms have developed resistance to pesticides. For example, it is estimated that more than 10 percent of all pest insect and mite species have become resistant to one or more types of pesticides (Brown, 1969). To further complicate pest management, most of these resistant species attack crop plants. Mosquito fish, a species of fish employed for mosquito control, have been observed to be resistant to several insecticides (Ferguson et al., 1965). These fish were collected in regions that had received heavy treatments of insecticides for pest control. The pine mouse has become resistant to endrin where insecticide treatment was intense (Webb and Horsfall, 1967).

Pesticides may under some circumstance have caused animals to be more susceptible to certain diseases. For instance, evidence gathered suggests that exposure of fish to sublethal levels of carbaryl and 2,4-D reduced their natural resistance to microsporidian parasites (Butler, 1969).

One of the harmful effects of pesticides, especially the chlorinated insecticides, results from the ability of certain organisms to concentrate these insecticides in their bodies. For example, eastern oysters have been noted to concentrate 1 part per billion of DDT in water to a level 70,000 times as great in their bodies (Butler, 1964). One species of fish was even more efficient; this species concentrated 0.25 ppb of DDT 100,000 times (Priester, 1965).

In summary, environmental pollution has resulted from the use of pesticides, although only 5 percent of the crop acres are treated with insecticides, 12 percent with herbicides, and 0.5 percent with fungicides. The organisms most seriously affected by pesticides include some species of beneficial insects, fishes, and birds. Of the estimated 200,000 species of plants and animals making up the life system in the United States, information on the effects of pesticides is available for less than 1 percent (Pimentel, 1971).

STRATEGIES FOR IMPROVEMENT

Benefits versus Damage

Monitoring to Determine Use Necessity (Predicting Pest Outbreaks and Crops Insurance)   Pesticides are sometimes applied to crops as a form of insurance: That is, the crop is treated with a pesticide on the chance that the pest may attack the crop. The disadvantages of this approach are numerous and include (1) high costs of treatment, (2) destruction of beneficial natural enemies, which frequently necessitates additional costly treatments, (3) environmental pollution, and (4) hazard to man.

Investigations are needed to determine the dynamics of insect populations so that outbreaks can be predicted. In the case of plant disease, a timely example exists of such an investigation: A mathematical simulator of Southern corn leaf blight was devised on the basis of data from laboratory observations of the pathogen and environment. In 1971, weekly simulations of blight were published for a national network that was promptly established for this purpose (Felch and Barger, 1971).

Unfortunately, a prediction system with the goal of decreasing pesticide use will sometimes predict no outbreak, only to have an outbreak occur. A single grower, of course, will be unwilling to use such a system and risk his crop for the general good of pollution control. If an insurance scheme could be developed, however, that would protect the grower against this risk, the prediction system should be more generally acceptable. The individual grower would be protected, and the public would benefit from reduced pollution and more economical disease and insect controls.

New Application Methods   Large quantities of some pesticides used for agricultural purposes are applied by either aircraft or ground equipment. Because of cost, convenience, and often necessity, many pesticides are generally applied by aircraft. It is estimated that 75–80 percent of all the commercial pesticide applications in California are made in this fashion. In areas where crops are grown on small plots, applications of pesticides are usually made by ground equipment.

Confinement of pesticides to the fields on which they are intended to be placed, or reduction of pesticide transport away from treated fields via air, water and soil is necessary if hazards associated with the use of agricultural chemicals are to be minimized. Akesson *et al.* (1971b) suggest four practical reasons why drift control of pesticide chemicals is of paramount importance in agriculture today.

1. Losses of chemicals from fields, varying from a few percent to as much as 75 percent of the applied material (Hindin *et al.*, 1966), reduce the amounts of chemical available to control the pests.

2. Hazards and disagreeable working conditions for equipment operators are of increasing concern, and drift-control systems can reduce this exposure, as well as reduce exposure to workers in nearby fields.

3. Drift-control technique can reduce the need for halting operations because of bad weather—usually wind, but also temperature inversions.

4. Lastly, drift control can reduce the potential for damage to nearby crops, damage to beneficial insect populations, and danger of residues higher than tolerances on nearby crops, as well as the hazards of general environmental contamination.

The basic physical formulations of pesticides available for plant protection are (1) dry materials as granules, microgranules and dusts; and (2) sprays as true solutions, wettable powders, encapsulated materials, and normal and inverted emulsions. Each of these has specific particle size ranges that largely control their application requirements, type of use, effectiveness, and their ability to become airborne and cause damage or excessive residues on nearby crops.

A close relationship exists between the factors of (1) spray particle size, (2) total volume applied, (3) type of spray coverage required and (4) the extent of drift or loss of small but significant amounts of spray from treatment areas to adjacent crops, animals, wildlife areas or human habitation. These factors are of primary importance to all types of spray applications, but are particularly significant when low volume (from one gallon to a few ounces per acre) applications of technical (no diluents other than those needed to dissolve or carry the toxicant) chemical are used (Akesson *et al.*, 1971a).

In order to minimize the use of pesticides without sacrificing efficiency and to confine the applied chemicals to the fields being treated, Akesson *et al.* (1971b) suggest the following:

1. *Dry granulars,* applied by air or ground either pre- or post-plant. They are primarily available now for weed and insect control. These usually must be worked into the soil to be effective.

2. *Coarse sprays*

    a. Produced by phase-crowded emulsions or by viscosity and foaming additives. These are of very limited use because of low distribution factor or very coarse drops—of 5000 μm volume median diameter (VMD) and over.

    b. Mechanically induced, which can be up to 5000 μm VMD, as from sprinkler cans, but are limited to around a maximum of 1500–2000 μm V M D when applied by aircraft, the exact size being dependent on aircraft speed. These are also limited in use by poor distribution of large drops.

c. Small drop size cutoff by various means. Presently only one commercial machine is available, the Microfoil boom. This can be used only with ground equipment and with helicopters flown at less than 60 mph. It is also of limited use because of low distribution of course drops around 800–1000 μm V M D, but drops under 800 μm are virtually eliminated.

3. *Ground operated equipment,* properly used. Drift from ground rigs with pressure nozzle systems can be greater than from aircraft; air-carrier sprayers, as used for orchard work, could be consistently worse than aircraft—although it depends in each case upon the degree of spray atomization used.

Hazards incurred by the use of agricultural chemicals can be reduced substantially if new and more effective ways can be developed for applying crop protection chemicals. One example of improved application has been the use of granular preparations of pesticides as a device to reduce drift. Until better techniques are developed, however, suitable regulations should be established to restrict spray particle size (by both aircraft and ground equipment) to the largest size compatible with effective pest control.

Bioenvironmental Control

Bioenvironmental control of pests involves manipulating the pest's environment or altering its physiology, genetics, and behavior, or employing these measures in combination to reduce populations to low densities (Pimentel *et al.,* 1965b). Methods for bioenvironmental control have been reviewed by Pimentel *et al.* (1965b), Knipling (1972) and the National Academy of Sciences (1969b). It should be pointed out that, with only 5 percent of the crop acres treated with insecticides, natural controls are in fact relied upon to limit most pest insects.

Breeding Resistance to Pests and Disease Utilizing natural resistance by selective breeding is a means of controlling pests and diseases that attack plants and animals. Although this method has been employed rather extensively in the control of plant diseases, it has had only limited use in insect control.

Resistance has only to be partial to be very effective. For example, reducing the rate of population growth of a pest could reduce the need of pesticide treatments. With lowered pesticide application, the natural enemies of the pest—parasites and predators—would be less endangered and could provide a measure of effective control of the pest.

Development of natural resistance to pests and disease will require the research efforts of geneticists and pest specialists. Research is slow, but the investment would most certainly be beneficial, for this is a long-range control and would tend to decrease the need for pesticides.

Use of Predators, Parasites, and Pathogens   Predators, parasites, and pathogens are effective control agents for animals existing in natural and agro-ecosystems. The use of these biological control agents has received much publicity in the popular press, but the investment in research has been limited.

Biological control has been effective in the control of some insect and weed pests. In the case of plant and animal diseases and parasites, the opportunities for biological control are limited because of the dangers involved in the replacement of one hazard with another.

Mention should be made of the possibility of "designing" parasites and predators for control of a specific pest by selective breeding. Man has been able to breed livestock and crop plants for specific purposes, so there is no reason to assume he cannot breed a specific parasite or predator for the control of a particular plant pest existing in the agro-ecosystem.

Genetic Manipulation (Lethal Genes) and Sexual Sterility   By manipulating the genetic makeup of pest species, population growth rates may be limited below economic injury levels. Lethal genes may be maintained in the population through the use of pest–plant gene complexes. Chromosome incompatibility may also be employed to reduce pest numbers to low levels. It might be possible to incorporate genes that cause an obligatory resting stage in the pest, thus limiting pest generations to one per year. With improved techniques of mass rearing of pests, these genetic manipulations look promising, especially for insect control.

Inducing sexual sterility in insects by means of radiation has had notable success in the control of the screwworm. The method has advantages for control of certain species, and research should be expanded to apply this control procedure to other species.

Use of Attractants and Repellents   Chemical stimuli play a dominant role in animal behavior, in many cases regulating feeding, mating, and oviposition behavioral patterns. Research on attractants has demonstrated that certain animal pests find their way to their plant or animal hosts by chemical attractants and stimulants present in these food hosts. Promising leads are available for application to some pest species, but most research needs to be done to extend this to other species. The specific sex attractants offer selective solutions to some pest problems, in particular those involving insect and mammal pests.

Such limited data as are available on oviposition attractants suggest opportunities for control, especially as related to insect pests. Also, behavioral studies of the response of insects, birds, and mammals to repellents may provide leads to additional control methods.

Environmental Manipulation   Many pest problems have been created by changes in agro-ecosystems that ultimately favored the pests. Altering the environment to make it less suitable may control pests or at least reduce their rates of increase. Environmental manipulation for pest control involves new approaches to plant spacing, species diversity, timing, crop rotation, plant hormones, water management, fertilizers, soil preparation, and sanitation. Various combinations of plant spacing, use of fertilizers, effective water management, and time of planting may contribute to pest control and should be investigated.

Plant Spacing   Pest damage to crops and forests can sometimes be reduced through changes in the spacing of the host plants. In this way the relative rates of growth of a plant and its pest population per unit time, and the behavior of the pest in searching for food, may be affected. When plants are closely spaced, the productivity of the plant population per unit time may be increased within certain limits. Placing the plants close together may add to the effectiveness of natural enemies and result in greater control of pest populations.

Species Diversity   Preliminary evidence suggests that pest populations reach outbreak levels more frequently on crops and forests placed under monoculture than on those grown naturally with a diversity of plant and animal species. Greater plant diversity supports greater animal diversity, thus helping to maintain the relative stability that exists under natural conditions. Diversity in parasites and predators—especially those feeding on one pest species—also contributes to greater stability in the population interactions, because each natural enemy has a different level of efficiency related to the density of the pest population. The use of the diversity technique has limitations with many crops because monoculture is essential in agricultural production. However, in certain situations, with the judicious selection of particular crop plants, it may be possible to reduce and in some cases control pests. In California the growing of alfalfa with cotton as a means to cotton-insect control offers promise, and other crop combinations could be developed through research.

Timing Some pests may be controlled successfully by growing the crops when the pest is not present, or injury may at least be reduced by selecting a planting date such that the most susceptible stage of crop development coincides with a low ebb in seasonal abundance of the pest. This technique employed with wheat has provided reasonably good control of the Hessian fly. Also, planting all the crop within a short period of time may overwhelm a pest population and prevent population buildups at the susceptible growth stage. Use of this technique can reduce the populations of plant pests by a generation or more each year. In any case, potential for pest control exists with this technique, and it deserves continued investigation for some crops and pests.

Crop Rotation Alternating the crops grown on farmland has long been a useful technique for control of the insects, nematodes, plant diseases, and weeds that become established with one crop and then increase in number with succeeding years. The tendency recently has been to cultivate the same crop on the same soil year after year and employ pesticides to offset the pest problems created. By planting crop plants that either are immune, or that in some other way cause the extinction of the pests associated with a particular crop, the cycle of pest increase can be broken, and need for control reduced or eliminated.

Plant Hormones The judicious use of plant hormones might alter plant growth or other plant characteristics to make the plant less appealing to pests, at the same time not adversely affecting production qualities. Several hormones that are in use change the characteristics of crop plants and later the survival of some pests attacking them.

Water Management Flooding fields may drown certain soil pests. Irrigation of fields during the winter season may cause some pests to emerge during the off-season and bring about their destruction. Epidemics in some pest populations might be brought about by properly timed irrigation of such crops.

Soil Preparation Tilling the soil at appropriate times is a simple, but highly effective, way of destroying soil pests that have vulnerable stages in their development. For example, it has been demonstrated that 98 percent of overwintering pupae of the corn earworm are destroyed by disturbing the soil during their sensitive resting stage. The abandonment of this cultural technique has often necessitated the use of pesticides as as substitute.

Sanitation and Destruction of Pest Inoculum Sanitation and the de-struction of inoculum in soil may serve to reduce infection and in some cases may thereby provide effective pest control. Even if this technique alone will not provide control, it could be valuable as a control supple-mentary to other control techniques.

Physical Environmental Factors Investigations have demonstrated that sound, light, and electromagnetic energy may attract, repel, and in some cases destroy invertebrate and vertebrate pests. For example, light flashes will interrupt the diapause of some insect pests, and low light in-tensity will prevent others from ovipositing. There is potential here for pest control in utilizing these and other physical factors, but little has been done to capitalize on it.

Integrated Control Integrated pest control has come to mean many things to many people. It is most accurately defined as a control method that encourages the conservation of predators and parasites along with the use of pesticidal agents. At present, information available as to the ecology of some pests and their enemies is sufficient to make possible a reduction in the amounts of pesticides used without sacrificing effi-ciency of pest control.

Fertilizers Host plant nutrition is known to affect the longevity and fecundity of a substantial number of invertebrates and plant pathogens, thus offering a means of pest control (Painter, 1951; Pimentel, 1965b; NAS, 1969b). For example, when potassium was applied along with nitrogen and phosphorus, the result was a reduction in the amount of sawfly-cutting in winter wheat. Also, corn grown in soil low in potas-sium appears to be more susceptible to Northern corn leaf blight. Hence, varying the amounts and ratios of fertilizers and other mineral elements that are provided to host plants can limit pest damage.

Cost Effects of Land–Insecticide Tradeoffs

Headley (1971) has proposed that a decrease in pesticide application would be possible, while maintaining a constant total production, with but a modest increase in the total land under cultivation. His general figure indicated that insecticide use could be reduced by at least 70 percent, perhaps as much as 80 percent, without loss of quality or total

output and that to do this would require a 10 percent increase in cultivated land.

Heady *et al.* (1972) prepared a computer routine and assigned coefficients relating yields and land use to estimates of loss from pest damage without use of chemicals. Pimental and Shoemaker (1972) applied
the Heady parameters based on linear programming and the Iowa State
Data Bank to estimate production cost of 11 farm products under various restrictions on land and insecticide use.

For corn and cotton, the tradeoffs of increased acreage and cost versus
loss due to insects were computed for complete withdrawal of insecticide treatment. For cotton, the parameters were present insecticide
schedule (USDA, 1970e) versus no insecticide treatment and land retirement program (USDA, 1970d) versus free land market. For 1967,
under the current pesticide treatment and land retirement program
(USDA, 1968a), the cost of cotton production was 23¢ per pound. The
computations for free land market are 14¢ per pound, using insecticides,
and 15¢ per pound without. The latter includes the additional expenses
of growing and harvesting 300,000 additional acres to offset the loss
due to insect action. Thus, the insecticide deletion is calculated to cost
1¢ per pound and the land retirement program 9¢, plus an additional 12¢
per pound support based on the 1967 data. The land retirement program
(USDA, 1970d), with about 60,000,000 acres of farm land diverted, results not only in lower yields per acre, but increase in total cost due to
the cultivation of less productive land. The total production figures for
1967 were 10,383,000 bales of cotton requiring 5.2 million acres. The
estimates under conditions of a free land market were that 4.4 million
acres would have been sufficient with insecticide treatment, whereas
4.7 million acres would be required without insecticides.

Tradeoff of Cosmetic Appearance for Safety

Several investigators, including Pimental, have suggested that attempts
to eliminate insects and insect parts completely from agricultural produce has increased pesticide application unnecessarily. For example, complete elimination of aphids and of holes in outer cabbage leaves requires
an inordinate increase in pesticide application. Similar statements have
been made in regard to elimination of *Drosophila* eggs from tomatoes
used in catsup and for thrips found on raspberries used in jam. Even
under present high insecticide use, however, some *Drosophila* eggs are
still to be found in all catsup and some thrips are in all raspberry jam.
The question has been posed—why not balance the threat to man's
health and safety posed by excessive and frequent pesticide application

against the disadvantage of a few insect parts on, or in, certain foods? A careful cost–benefit analysis is proposed.

Systems Approach to Pest Control

Because there is no simple answer or single technique for pest control, there is need for a systems approach to this complex problem. This approach includes (1) application of ecological principles in crop culture and pest management, (2) a cost–benefit analysis of pertinent economic factors, and (3) quantitative methods involving mathematical analysis and computer technology.

The systems approach would effectively deal with the diverse factors involved in crop culture and also with situations wherein several pests attack a particular crop (Watt, 1964). With the systems approach, pest management becomes an integral part of the total crop-culture program and includes the other crops grown in the region. This type of pest control requires an understanding of the basic mechanisms affecting the crop and the interactions of various factors such as pest, crop plant, water, soil, and fertilizers. Included in the systems analysis, in addition to crop-cultural practices, are the economics, the public health aspects, and the environmental quality of the system. Only then can the total risks and benefits of the factors in the system be evaluated and used as a basis for making sound decisions about pest control measures.

The tools of systems analysis and computer technology are an invaluable aid in dealing with the many interactions in crop systems. Initially, only the major pests need be included in a pest-management program; then, as additional information is gathered, a more complete and sophisticated pest-management program could be developed for the crop and the region.

BIODEGRADABILITY AND DEGRADATION PRODUCTS

Opposition to the use of pesticides has been based upon three properties that vary greatly in importance from one type of compound to another—toxicity, persistence and accumulation in the food chain. Chlorinated hydrocarbon insecticides tend to degrade slowly in the environment and are soluble in body fat. Therefore, they can persist in the environment and are concentrated by animals and man through the food chain. Organophosphate insecticides are generally not very persistent, but since they are more acutely toxic they present greater occupational hazards. They are also more expensive, and because they are not so persistent, require repeated applications to achieve adequate control. According to the second report of the Council on Environmental Quality (1971), there has been a trend toward using less persistent but more toxic pesticides; this, it is stated, should relieve adverse environmental effects but might result in a higher incidence of accidental poisonings.

In this section of the report, the three objectionable features of pesticides identified above will be considered. Their impact on the environment will be related to the ability of living organisms, especially microbes, to degrade both natural and man-made organic compounds. It will then be apparent that those features of chemical structure that make for tolerable persistence in pesticides, yet allow for retainment of essential biological action, cannot be defined with certainty. This is due, in turn, to the fact that knowledge of the degradative capabilities and limitations of microbes is incomplete. It may also be noted that, in speaking of the chemical research and development of new pesticides, Dr. Richard Wegler of Farbenfabriken Bayer AG has observed that "10–20 percent of the chemists, which in my opinion is far too few, base their work on fundamental biological knowledge" (Wegler, 1971).

Toxicity

Any chemical compound that is singled out for its toxic action against a pest is unlikely to be completely inactive against other forms of life, including man. However, the important question to consider is the dosage required to produce toxic effects. Long-term toxicological studies have been a routine part of pesticide research and development for many years; Naegele (1971) has tabulated the numerous safety evaluation studies that currently must be undertaken before an agricultural chemical can be registered. These tests, of course, include residue analysis on food crops, meat and milk, in addition to studies of the effects of pesticides on laboratory animals. It has been stated (Wegler, 1971) that if these requirements were strictly applied to foodstuffs there would be far-reaching restrictions, or even bans, that would probably include coffee, tea and alcoholic drinks. The point to be emphasized is that such prohibition would be unjustified since harmful effects are produced only if these and similar beverages are taken in excessive amounts.

There is a widespread public misapprehension to the effect that compounds found in nature are harmless, whereas chemicals introduced by man invariably involve hazards. Even those members of the public who can recall that deadly poisons are present in certain fungi, and as alkaloids in many plants, may still be unaware that our daily food contains real or potential toxicants that occur naturally. Crosby (1969) has observed that "eating represents the greatest direct exposure to exotic compounds that most of us ever receive." Indeed, the Symposium on Natural Food Toxicants (American Chemical Society, 1969) considered many natural compounds that belong to categories associated exclusively in the public mind with manufactured products. These included a class of herbicides and fish poisons (furocoumarins, present in certain plants), a plant growth regulator (indoleacetic acid), insecticide-like compounds found in carrot and potato, and a variety of fungicides, bacteriocides and antibiotics.

The extent of the problem cannot be evaluated on the basis of toxicity alone. No chemical compound of biological origin will progressively accumulate in an environment, such as soil, where microbes are able to grow. Whatever the nature of the compound, provided it was synthesized by an organism during life, and released at death to the environment, it will also have served as an energy source for the growth of microorganisms during the course of evolution. Given a long enough time, it is possible also that some microbial strains may acquire the ability to degrade those chemicals that man has dispersed through the environment. However, microbes have been present on the earth and exposed to biochemicals for 2–3 billion years, whereas modern industry and agriculture have supplied them with novel substrates only during the last 100 years or so. And, although microbes are not the sole agency for removal of man-made chemicals from the biosphere, they are probably the most important. These compounds, if not degraded, will accumulate in the environment. By contrast, atropine, a natural product that is much more toxic than most pesticides, is readily degraded by certain soil microorganisms (Niemer *et al.*, 1959; Niemer and Bucherer, 1961).

Concentration of Pesticides Through Food Chains

As a very persistent pesticide such as D D T accumulates, it will not be uniformly distributed in the environment. Thus, taking the weight of seawater on the earth's surface as 3.09×10^{21} pounds, it would take 10,000 years at the present rate of production (309 million pounds annually) to reach the saturation level of D D T in water quoted by Bowman *et al.* (1960) of about 1 ppb. However, only the upper 100 meters of seawater are homogenized by the action of winds. When this factor is taken into account, it may be estimated that 38-times the total production of D D T to date would be required to saturate those parts of the ocean that are accessible (Goldberg *et al.*, 1971). We may contrast these theoretical predictions with the actual conditions of a body of water not in equilibrium with the oceans, e.g. Lake Michigan. The average rate of water retention in this lake is 30.8 years and its volume is 4,871 cubic kilometers

(Rainey, 1967) so that, even if no more DDT were to enter the lake, the pesticide it contains at present would not be cleared away for several generations. The main ecological problem stems from the fact that chlorinated hydrocarbons are lipid-partitioning substances and are concentrated along a food chain. Thus, the concentration of DDT in bottom muds of Lake Michigan is about 0.014 ppm. The amphipods contain 0.41 ppm, fish such as coho and lake trout 3–6 ppm , and herring gulls—at the top of the food chain—up to 99 ppm (Harrison et al., 1970). The increase in concentration so achieved is about seven thousand fold. With regard to the mixed layer (the upper 100 m) of the oceans, Goldberg et al. (1971) have pointed out that enrichment is likely to occur in the surface film of the sea, which contains fatty acids and alcohols. If this is so, DDT may be stripped from this film by bacteria and phytoplankton and thus enter food chains. These authors report concentrations of DDT residues as high as 10 ppm in sea birds that feed on planktonic organisms far from land. In coastal areas, higher but variable concentrations are to be expected.

The ability of the food chain to concentrate chlorinated hydrocarbons has received wide publicity; but it is less generally appreciated that this phenomenon-like toxic action is also characteristic of certain compounds found in nature, as well as of those made by man. The behavior of the isoprenoid alkane, pristane, is an instructive example both for its similarities with DDT and for one crucial difference—its susceptibility to attack by bacteria. Pristane is formed by crustaceans of the genus *Calanus* from the phytol moiety of chlorophyll present in the algae they ingest (Avigan and Blumer, 1968). Since calanid copepods function as an important link in the marine food chain, it is thought that their synthesis of pristane is the most significant source of this hydrocarbon in both animal tissues and in geological formations. The pristane content of the digestive tract of the basking shark is indicative of food sources and feeding grounds; analysis for this and related hydrocarbons may be generally useful in studies of the movements of marine animals (Blumer, 1967). Judged solely by the inability of a range of species to metabolize pristane, therefore, the compound is not biodegradable and also concentrates in lipids. However, like other hydrocarbons, pristane will accumulate unchanged only in those locations where it is not susceptible to microbial attack; given favorable conditions, it is readily metabolized by a variety of microorganisms (McKenna and Kallio, 1971). This is not surprising, since the molecule of pristane is constructed from reduced isoprene units, and a great number of natural products, which have long served as sources of carbon and energy for microbes, are biosynthesized from such units. It is significant that these organisms usually fail to metabolize a man-made chemical structure in which a methyl group has been moved away from its isoprenoid position, particularly when it becomes attached to a carbon atom already bound to three others (McKenna and Kallio, 1964).

Persistence

Pesticides may be removed from the area of application by several processes, some of which are dependent upon environmental factors to such an extent as to render the term *half life* meaningless unless conditions are carefully defined (Lichtenstein, 1972). A compound may be observed to "disappear" when it has merely moved elsewhere. For example, it may be transported by leaching from a field in Wisconsin to Lake Michigan, where its presence is no less objectionable. It may vaporize from water surfaces (Acree *et al.*, 1963) and from plants and soils (Nash and Beall, 1970), and after passing through the atmosphere, may be deposited on distant territory by rainfall (Tarrant and Tatton, 1968; Yates *et al.*, 1970). Or it may not move far: It may be sorbed on soil particles until this reservoir is saturated. By this means the pesticide, though out of sight and mind, has merely been swept under the environmental carpet.

The ultimate destruction and removal of pesticides from the biosphere is mainly dependent upon microbial action, although photooxidation is also important (Crosby, 1971). Volatile organic compounds undergo numerous changes on exposure to ultraviolet radiation, and, as Crosby has suggested, the atmosphere may act as a huge photochemical furnace that can "burn" compounds such as pesticides to nontoxic products. However, the contribution of such a process to overall pesticide disappearance has not been assessed. What is more certain is that radiation may rapidly modify chemical structure and toxicity. The rapid photooxidation of pyrethrins (Chen and Casida, 1969) and rotenone (Jones and Haller, 1931; Cahn *et al.*, 1945) has virtually restricted these low-hazard compounds to those applications (e.g., indoor aerosol sprays) where losses due to sunlight are unimportant. Moreover, photooxidation may increase hazard. The chlorinated hydrocarbon aldrin is readily oxidized to the more toxic dieldrin (Rosen and Sutherland, 1967) and parathion is converted into the extremely poisonous paraoxon, although subsequent reactions in the presence of light reduce the overall toxicity (Frawley *et al.*, 1958).

Biodegradability

Many organic compounds that are degraded slowly, if at all, by plants and animals can be oxidized to carbon dioxide by soil microorganisms, and so serve as sources of carbon and energy for their growth. A man-made compound will be biodegradable if it is susceptible to attack by the enzymic apparatus acquired by microbes during the course of evolution. This, in turn, depends upon two factors: first, the ability of microbial enzymes to accept as substrates compounds having chemical structures similar to, but not identical with, those found in nature; and second, the ability of these novel substrates, when in the presence of microbes, to induce or derepress the synthesis of the necessary degradative enzymes. Biodegradability is less likely to be achieved by incorporating into a pesticide molecule structural features that are never encountered in natural products. Conversely, when, for example, the *para* chlorine atoms of DDT are replaced by methoxyl groups—very common substituents of the benzene nucleus in natural products—the resulting pesticide, methoxychlor, is much more readily metabolized by microbes than was the original DDT.

Some of the main metabolic features of soil microbes that enable them to utilize organic chemicals that other organisms fail to degrade will now be outlined. But first it should be noted that aerobic bacteria employ most of the biochemical sequences and cycles that occupy a central position in metabolic maps and are generally to be found in other living forms. Their unique biochemical assets lie in their ability to catalyze early steps in degradation that other organisms cannot accomplish, and by these reactions to form metabolites that can then enter the common pathways of metabolism, such as the Krebs cycle or the fatty acids "spiral." Thus, as alkane remains a biochemically inert molecule until a terminal carbon is oxidized; the fatty acid so formed may then enter a main channel of metabolism, namely β-oxidation. A saturated ring-structure is also inert until a hydroxyl group is inserted, and, if this occurs at an appropriate point in the molecule, the possibility then arises that further oxidation may break the ring and provide fragments that can be degraded. The unsubstituted benzene nucleus is an inert resonance structure, but suitably substituting two hydroxyl groups enables enzymic ring-fission to occur. The oxidizing agent in these reactions is molecular oxygen—one atom of oxygen is incorporated into the compound and the other atom is reduced to water. In the cells of other living organisms, oxidations almost invariably occur by removal of hydrogen atoms from their substrates, but microbes possess to an exceptional degree the ability to oxidize by inserting oxygen, and in so doing they can initiate the degradation of substrates that other living forms cannot metabolize. These reactions are catalyzed by oxygenases, a group of enzymes that has been well reviewed by Hayaishi (1966, 1969). For a compound to be biodegradable, therefore, it is clearly important that the site of action of an oxygenase should not be blocked by a substituent. Among the structures attacked by these enzymes are methoxyl groups, and the biodegradability of methoxychlor may be attributed to this readily metabolized "handle."

Although far from complete, knowledge is now available relating to the microbial degradation of the benzene nucleus, a component of the molecules of many pesticides. After two hydroxyl groups have been inserted to give a dihydric phenol, another oxygenase (a dioxygenase) cleaves the nucleus by incorporating both of the atoms of molecular oxygen into the substrate. A large number of pathways for the complete degradation of the compound now become available, depending upon the structure of the dihydric phenol and the point of action of the dioxygenase. A recent review (Dagley, 1971) has summarized our current knowledge of these pathways, the differing capacities of the enzymes to tolerate substituent groups in their substrates, and the abilities of various chemical compounds to serve as inducers of these enzymes in microbes.

Some of this accumulated wealth of knowledge should be relevant to the task of designing pesticides of suitable biodegradability. Guesses based upon theoretical chemical considerations are no substitute for the findings of biological investigations, as the following example will show. The enzyme fumarase catalyzes hydration of fluorofumarate to give α-fluoromalate, from which H^+ and F^- ions are immediately expelled to give oxaloacetate (Clarke *et al.*, 1968). This hydration is predicted on purely chemical grounds by Markownikoff's rule. However, chlorofumarate and other halogenofumarates are hydrated the other way round, to give β-substituted malates. The halogen is not expelled. The intervention of the enzyme gives an unexpected result—one that is not predicted from electron density distributions for molecules when they are not bound to the enzyme (Teipel *et al.*, 1968). It may also be noted that a simplistic view based on bond energies would be inadequate, since the strong C-F bond in the substrate is broken, and the weaker C-Cl bond is not.

The most instructive studies to date of reactions that involve the expulsion of chlorine from substrates are those concerned with the microbial metabolism of the hormonal herbicides 4-chlorophenoxyacetate (CPA), 4-chloro-2-methylphenoxyacetate (MCPA) and 2,4-dichlorophenoxyacetate (2,4-D). These compounds are biodegradable, and will serve as the sole sources of carbon for growth of certain bacteria. First, the side-chains of 2,4-D (Tiedje and Alexander, 1969) and MCPA (Gamar and Gaunt, 1971) are released as glyoxylate, leaving chlorinated phenols. The enzymes catalyzing these reactions appear to be monooxygenases. It is significant that in every system studied the nucleus of each chlorocatechol, formed in the next degradative step, is cleaved by an *ortho* dioxygenase; for this pathway involves a lactonization that results in the expulsion of chlorine. Thus, 4-chlorocatechol, formed from CPA, gives β-chloromuconic acid that loses Cl^- on lactonization (Evans *et al.*, 1971). A similar sequence was shown for MCPA (Gaunt and Evans, 1971), and experiments with purified lactonizing enzyme indicated that the reaction was a single-step dehydrochlorination. The data of Tiedje *et al.* (1969) also indicate that one of the chlorines of 3,5-dichlorocatechol, formed during the metabolism of 2,4-D, is likewise expelled when *cis,cis*-2,4-dichloromuconic acid lactonizes.

These studies show how, and probably why, species of *Pseudomonas* and *Arthrobacter* can tolerate the introduction of chlorine into molecules that accordingly remain biodegradable. On the other hand, there have been numerous fragmentary reports of the failures of microbes to metabolize halogen-substituted molecules to completion. Indeed, one long-established method of delineating a degradative sequence is to make a chemical substitution in the compound under investigation. When the new compound is now exposed to adapted bacteria, the cell suspension will be able to catalyze degradative steps until a point is reached at which an enzymic reaction is blocked by the presence of the substituent. A compound will then accumulate in culture fluids, and can therefore be isolated and identified; this compound will be an analogue of a "natural" substrate. Wedemeyer (1967) found that soil microorganisms were capable of metabolizing DDT to the extent of removing a number of chlorine atoms to give such compounds as *p,p′*-dichlorodiphenylmethane and *p,p′*-dichlorobenzophenone. Focht and Alexander (1970) showed that these compounds are "cometabolized" by *Hydrogenomonas* and hence how DDT might be substantially, if not completely, degraded by the combined action of various microbial species in the environment.

Information obtained from the study of microbial metabolism of very persistent pesticides has been largely negative; it is a record of microbial failures. It warns us of features of molecular architecture that should be avoided, and in this respect is valuable. But when less sophisticated measurements of its rate of disappearance have already determined that a pesticide is not significantly biodegradable, and when other observations have confirmed its widespread persistence and distribution in the environment, then it would clearly be better to use existing knowledge in an attempt to find an effective replacement.

Metcalf, his colleagues, and others have devised and thoroughly tested an experimental method that promises to aid such searches. This technique will be briefly discussed.

A Model Ecoystsem for Evaluating Pesticides

This approach (Metcalf *et al.*, 1971) meets the need for a laboratory method whereby new pesticides can be screened for their environmental fate. A model ecosystem, providing a 7-element food chain, is developed in glass aquaria 10 X 12 X 20 in. with 160 sq in. of surface. Each tank contains white quartz sand molded into a sloping soil–air–water interface. A major requirement in developing the scheme was to choose appropriate organisms that would be available throughout the year and could be readily reared under the conditions of the aquarium. Details on these points are given by the study. ^{14}C-DDT, when applied to an equivalent rate of one pound per acre, was found to accumulate in mosquito larvae, snails, and fish as DDE, DDD and DDT and concentrated from 10,000- to 100,000-fold. These results, obtained with DDT after 1 month in the food chains of the model system, show an excellent approximation to conditions observed after many years in nature. Very different results were obtained with analogues of DDT in which chlorine in the benzene nucleus was replaced by groups such as methoxyl and methyl. As previously noted, such groups are susceptible to attack by monooxygenases and therefore provide biodegradable "handles." After oxidation, the lipid-partitioning compounds become more water soluble and may be conjugated and eliminated. The oxygenases involved are especially active in vertebrate liver. In particular, higher animals have a substantial advantage over insects in the metabolism of xenobiotics (Terriere, 1968). The studies of DDT analogues using the model ecosystem showed that, in contrast to DDT, the concentration factors from water to fish were: methiochlor, 0; methylchlor, 100; methoxychlor, 1500; and ethoxychlor, 1540 (Kapoor *et al.*, 1970, 1971). The very low ratio of nonpolar to polar metabolites found in the fish, compared with the corresponding ratio for DDT, was another indication of biodegradability. It may be observed that compounds degraded by the organisms of the model ecosystem are most unlikely to resist attack by microbes. A compound of this type that is not concentrated in the food chain will not persist in the soil.

CAN MICROBES KEEP PACE WITH MAN?

Microbes have had at their disposal a time span of billions of years in which to acquire the ability to metabolize organic natural products. Organic chemists have been contributing novel substances for only a century or so, and the biosphere has received the products of their ingenuity in significant amounts only in the last 20 years. How long will it take microbes to acquire the ability to destroy these compounds?

A pessimist, pointing first to a metabolic chart on the wall of his laboratory and then to a row of Beilsteins in his bookcase, would stress the relatively narrow range of compounds involved in living processes compared with the number that are man-made. However, this comparison exaggerates the scope of our knowledge of metabolism. The pursuit of biochemical truth has seldom been completely disinterested, for it has centered on man and his problems, and there are thousands of complex molecules that, though synthesized by plants, remain outside the mainstream of biochemistry because we know nothing of their enzymology. And whenever a complex molecule is biosynthesized in the plant kingdom there are, by this time, microbes waiting in the soil to utilize it. It is certain that large numbers of intriguing enzymic reactions catalyzed by microbes are not yet discovered; we cannot, therefore, evaluate completely even the present scope of degradative versatility in microbes.

An optimist would point to genetic changes, produced in bacteria over the time span of a few laboratory experiments, through which organisms have acquired the ability to catalyze new degradative pathways. In this connection the experiments of Wu et al. (1968) will be outlined briefly. Originally, the organism they used (Aerobacter aerogenes) could not metabolize xylitol, but this was made possible by its acquisition of the ability to transform xylitol to xylulose, a pentose that is rapidly metabolized. Xylitol was converted to xylilose by a dehydrogenase that is normally used to oxidize a "natural" substrate, ribitol. Three successive mutations gave cells that synthesized an altered enzyme catalyzing the rapid dehydrogenation of xylitol, and that also effectively transported this substrate to the enzyme site.

It may be that, eventually, microbes may acquire the ability to degrade man-made chemicals that presently persist in the biosphere. In the sequence of events described by Wu et al., one step towards this acquisition appears to be rendered more feasible by the fact, referred to earlier, that a few of the batteries of bacterial degradative enzymes that might be modified are already known to accept a range of homologous compounds as substrates. It remains to be seen whether the process of selection could be speeded up by exposing mutants to novel substrates, or better, to the compounds that intelligent speculation would predict to be degradative intermediates in the event that the novel compound became biodegradable. Chakrabarty and Gunsalus (1970, 1971) have discovered that functionally related catabolic genes, borne on plasmids, can be transferred from one bacterial species to another; therefore, it is probable that if one species found a way to metabolize a hitherto recalcitrant pesticide, the information would be acquired by other species.

Microorganisms are the most important of the agents affecting the complete removal of pesticide residues from the environment. Each organism employs the same enzyme apparatus as is used for degrading natural products; accordingly, the biodegradability of a pesticide, at least in soil, is determined by the capabilities and limitations of microbial enzymes. The study of microbial enzymes that degrade all types of natural products should be fostered in order to provide a scientific framework for reference in the search for less recalcitrant pesticides. Investigations concerned with the extremely sluggish degradation of some pesticides in current use might continue, but chiefly in the hope of being able to foster genetic changes—should this be possible—that would equip microbes to clear these residues from the environment at some future date.

4

Fertilizer

The critical role of fertilizer was stated a century ago by Professor Levi Stockbridge before the Massachusetts Agricultural Board:

If we are to support our present dense population, if we are to supply food with the present condition of our soil, we must go outside our home resources to do so. Up to this hour, farming in the United States has not been a proper culture, but a system of spoilation. Our population in the future must either starve or we must adopt another course (Flint, 1873).

The validity of Professor Stockbridge's statement predated the current extensive use of inorganic fertilizers. The developed countries do and must augment the inadequate native supplies of the primary plant nutrients—nitrogen, phosphorus, potassium—if they are to produce the increasing quantities of food they require (Ibach and Mahon, 1968).

FERTILITY TRENDS AND CROP PRODUCTION

The continuous use of soil without replacement of the essential nutrients removed by crops, and its indiscriminate use as a sink for waste materials, leads inevitably to lower productive capacity. The loss of productive soil through thoughtless and unplanned practices must be minimized if future generations are to continue the production of abun-

52

dant food for increasing populations. Natural soils vary widely in levels of essential nutrients as well as in the ability to supply them for plant growth. Fertility is influenced both by the nutrient content of the parent material and the various processes of weathering that lead to soil formation. Thus, some areas possess soils of high fertility, while others have only limited native crop producing capacity. The great challenge of management is to increase the quality of the poorly productive soils and to maintain the high capacity of the fertile ones in order to maximize crop production on each.

Erosion by wind and water reduces significantly the fertility and productivity of the soil. Wind erosion is estimated to move as much as 30 million tons of soil into the atmosphere as dust each year in the United States (Wadleigh, 1968; Wadleigh and Dyal, 1970). Whatever fraction is finely divided into nutrient-rich particles and is finally deposited on non-agricultural areas represents a net loss in soil fertility. In many cases this represents a significantly large fraction of the total potential. Water erosion is estimated to move into streams and reservoirs, as sediment, at least 4 billion tons of soil each year in the United States (Wadleigh, 1968). This is equivalent to a 6-inch layer from 4 million acres. Erosion is a selective process—the fine, nutrient-laden mineral particles and the organic matter are lost first. In addition, water erosion dissolves and carries away a disproportionately large amount of plant nutrients from the richer agricultural soils. Thus, to maintain the productive capacity of our soils, the nutrient losses from erosion must be replaced annually in addition to those removed in crops.

Modern agriculture, with its high crop yields, is based on there being a supply of nutrients as fertilizer equal to those removed. Wadleigh and Dyal (1970) state that soils have been "systematically" and "unfavorably altered" by depletion of nutrients. Stanford *et al.* (1970) estimated that, in the past 100 years, 35 billion tons of organic material containing 1.75 billion tons of organic nitrogen, have been lost from the top 40 inches of cropped agricultural soils in the United States. Black (1968) states that during early farming years the midwestern prairie soils released 200–400 pounds of nitrate-nitrogen per acre annually. In terms of these historical losses, current fertilizer additions are small. For example, Martin *et al.* (1970) estimated that on the approximately 18 million acres of cropland in Minnesota, the total annual nitrogen withdrawals average close to a million tons. Withdrawals of phosphorus averaged approximately a fifth that amount, or two tenths of a million tons. Less than one fourth of this amount is added annually as fertilizers. If one takes into account the nutrients added in manures and by legumes and estimates crop use efficiency at less than 50 percent, the addition of chemical fertilizers at two- to three-times the present rates could be justified in terms of improved crop yields.

These data support the prediction that, to maintain the crop production levels presently enjoyed in the United States, fertilizer levels must be increased. The challenge lies in finding application methods that maximize the use of plant nutrients on the productive land and avoid loss to the environment beyond the immediate productive unit. Frink (1971) has emphasized the prime need, to focus on the development and implementation of fertilizer application methods that supply fertilizer in the amounts required for effective crop production and to ensure their efficient use for crop growth. Data supporting these contentions with reference to total and to specific crops are found in Tables 7 and 8. Over the past 25 years, total crop production in the United States has increased nearly 30 percent and the per-acre yields nearer to 50 percent; thus, during the years since 1947 the acreage under cultivation has declined steadily. The figures projected to 1980 predict a further 30-percent increase in yield and total production without appreciable change in acreage under cultivation, assuming land use similar to 1970 over the next decade. The data of Table 8 pertain to the increase in yields of specific crops over the last 15 years, with projections to 1980. The conclusions are similar to those gathered from Table 7–the annual increments of increase are summarized at the base of the table. It is clear that corn, sorghum grain and cotton have responded most notably to changing agricultural practices; it is generally predicted that this response will continue through the decade. Although the increases in wheat and soybean yields

TABLE 7   United States Crop Production with Acreages, Yields and Projections to 1980

Years	Production Index[a]	Index Per Acre[a]	Actual Number of Acres in Use[b] (1,000,000 acres)
1947–1949	91	86	379
1957–1959	100	100	357
1967–1969	119	126	339
1970	119	127	337
1980 (estimated)	147	156[c]	337[c]
		149[d]	352[d]

SOURCE: (Durost, 1971).
[a] Data relative to 1957–1959 yield (base index = 100).
[b] Primarily planted acres, orchards, groves, vineyards and summer fallow.
[c] From projections on individual crop yields.
[d] Using 1960–1969 trends.

TABLE 8   United States Yields of Specific Crops (per harvested acre)

Period	Years	Corn (bushels)	Sorghum Grain (bushels)	Wheat (bushels)	Soybeans (bushels)	Cotton (lb)
1	1957–1959	51	33	23.6	23.6	438
2	1967–1969	80	53	28.4	26.2	466
3	1970	76	50	31.2	27.2	456
4	1980 (est.)	109	76	35.2	31.0	560
Average Annual Increases						
1–2		2.9	2.0	0.5	0.3	2.8
2–4		2.4	1.9	0.6	0.4	7.8

SOURCE: (Durost, 1971).

over the past 15 years have been reasonable, the incremental change has been exceedingly small. Clearly, more study is needed in the case of these two important crops and should be vigorously pursued—whether in the areas of genetics or crop practices, or both.

FERTILIZER CONSUMPTION PATTERNS

The use of inorganic fertilizers has been increasing in the United States since about 1800. The size of the fertilizer business, as indicated by sales volume, had reached 1.8 billion dollars by 1966 and nearly 2 billion dollars by 1970 (USDA, 1970d). In actual plant nutrients added to the United States soils, the rate of increase has been at about 10 percent per year. The reasons for increased fertilizer consumption are no doubt primarily economic. Hildreth and Williams (1968) pinpoint as significant factors the "interaction of other technology with fertilizer production, increased farmer knowledge, prices and above all availability."

During the past decade or two a fertilizer-dependent agriculture has developed throughout the United States (Heady *et al.,* 1965). Contributing causes have been a shortage of farm labor and a national farm policy that induced farmers to strive for higher yields on fewer acres to maintain their economic viability. Increase in farm output over the 35-year period, 1930–1965, and changes in farm input responsible for the production gains, are shown in Table 9. The data are stated relative to the years 1957–1959, taken as a base index = 100. As implied earlier, the farm output essentially doubled with but a small change in the total of farm real estate in use. An approximate decrease in farm labor to one third is marginally offset by a threefold increase in power and machinery

TABLE 9   Subgroups of Total Farm Inputs and Outputs in United States[a]

| | Output | | | Input | | | |
Year	Total	Labor	Land	Machinery and Power	Ferti- lizer	Feed, Seed, Livestock	Miscel- laneous
1930-1934	60	210	88	35	15	24	76
1940	70	192	92	42	23	45	73
1950	86	142	97	86	55	72	85
(1951-1959)	100	100	100	100	100	100	100
1960	106	92	100	100	111	109	106
1964	112	79	102	101	159	123	120
1965	115	75	100	101	167	124	124

SOURCE: USDA Statistical Bulletin 233, Revised July, 1966.
[a] Data relative to inputs and outputs for 1951-1959 (base index = 100).

use. By far the largest change, more than tenfold over the period, has been in fertilizer utilization. The largest percentage increase of the first 20 years accrued in the 1940-1950 decade; more recently, application has at least doubled each decade, with increasing emphasis on nitrogen (see Figure 1). From Table 9 one also notes a fivefold increase in feed and livestock inputs and a doubling of unspecified miscellaneous inputs.

Nelson (1972) tabulated the absolute amounts of fertilizer consumption in the United States, as well as the amounts of the three prime nutrients—nitrogen, phosphorus, and potassium. In millions of tons, the figures increased from about 24.5 to 40 over the period 1954-1970. Again, the increase was predominantly in the use of nitrogen. Using the

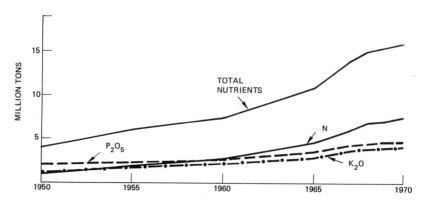

FIGURE 1   Plant nutrient consumption. (Fertilizer Summary Data, TVA, 1970.)

1955 and 1970 figures, the nitrogen increase (in millions of tons) was from under 2 to 7.3; phosphorus, as P_2O_5, from 2.2 to 4.5; and potassium, as K_2O, from 1.6 to 2.5. Thus, the fertilizer used in 1970 totalled over 16 million tons of N, P_2O_5 and K_2O. The acceleration in use has changed in recent years—the total increase from 1960 to 1968 was nearly 70 percent (or by 5 million tons) in 8 years compared to a total of 4.7 million tons in the previous 15 years (1945-1960). Nelson (1972) predicts a more modest expansion of fertilizer utilization in the United States in the decade 1970–1980 than in the past decade to reach an annual application of about 23 million tons of plant nutrients by 1980.

The increased fertilizer input, with consequent increased production per acre, has permitted an actual decrease in acreage under cultivation over the past 40 years (1930–1970) that amounts to nearly 50 million acres (Ibach and Mahon, 1968).

The strong trend to increased fertilizer application is not uniform across the United States. In the 10-year period 1955–1965, the use per harvested acre still averaged under 100 pounds. As one would expect, the amount of fertilizer used varied vastly among the crops in relation to cash value per acre. In addition, the variation by region and individual farm area was wide. Figure 2 illustrates the use distribution for the year 1968. The South Atlantic states show the highest average, about 275 pounds per harvested acre. The averages of utilization for nine regions of the United States for 1970 are shown in Table 10.

In the breakdown by crop, corn accounts for about 40 percent of the total plant nutrients applied in the United States. Second is hay and pasture, which account for approximately 15 percent of the total. In

TABLE 10   United States Fertilizer Use in 1968[a]

Region	Average (lb/acre)
Pacific	141
Mountain	46
West South Central	71
West North Central	67
East South Central	148
East North Central	137
South Atlantic	277
Middle Atlantic	117
New England	158

[a] Adapted from Fertilizer Summary Data, TVA, 1970.

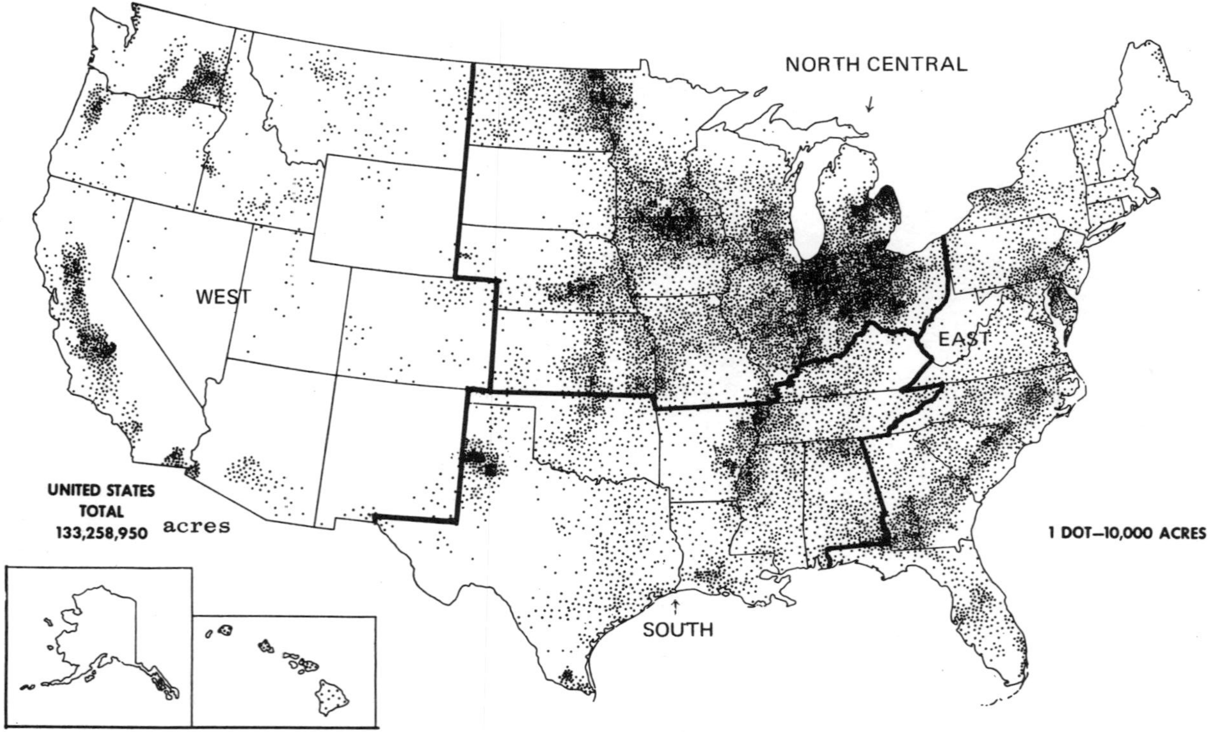

FIGURE 2 United States fertilizer use pattern, 1968. (Fertilizer Summary Data, TVA, 1970.)

this case, the extensive acreage held in pasture land rather than high rates of application is responsible. Third is cotton, at about 8 percent. It is clear that the crops with the highest value per unit of land will justify the highest fertilizer application rate. For example, in 1964, according to Ibach and Mahon (1968), potatoes averaged 400 kg/ha (kg/ha X 0.89 = lb/acre); nuts, 322; vegetables, 318; and sugar beets, 280. In each case, over 100 kg/ha each of nitrogen and phosphorus were added. In certain agricultural areas, specific crops receive even higher rates of fertilizer application. Among these are vegetables, citrus crops in Florida and Texas, tobacco, certain irrigated lands in the West, and high value vegetable crops along the east coast.

The increases in fertilizer consumption in the United States are expected to come largely from higher rates of application in areas now at the lower end of the use scale. Some, perhaps many, of the highly cultivated lands that are high fertilizer-use areas and some crops, for example corn, appear to have approached the maximum profitable rate of application. Little additional fertilizer consumption is anticipated for these crops over the next 20 years.

PROJECTIONS OF FERTILIZER USE

Future applications of plant nutrients in the United States are difficult to predict with a high degree of confidence. Attempts to predict use levels, by decades, over the last quarter of the twentieth century are particularly difficult in view of the uncertainties of changing technological advances and newer societal constraints. Berry (1971) considers most projections to be on the high side. Factors tending to slow the growth in rates of application are (1) efforts of suppliers to obtain higher prices and to bring current excess production capacity into line with demand, and (2) more active concern over, and possible restriction by environmental agencies of, added nutrients in runoff from fertilized agricultural land. The prime factors tending to increase fertilizer use are changes in farm organization and new technologies.

Table 11 lists four sets of projections of United States fertilizer use by 1980. Though obtained by different procedures, each has assumed that the real price of fertilizer will continue to decline and the production capacity remain more than adequate to meet the demand. The estimates are surprisingly alike, though the error range in two cases is substantial.

All authorities agree that plant nutrients must be added to the soil if there is to be adequate food on the American table. A great deal has been written to document the essentiality of fertile soils to supply the basic goods needed by mankind (for example, see Aldrich *et al.*, 1970).

TABLE 11   United States Fertilizer Use: 1980 Projections by Nutrient

Forecast Source	Nitrogen (N)[a] (1,000,000 tons)	Phosphates (P$_2$O$_5$)[a] (1,000,000 tons)	Potash (K$_2$O)[a] (1,000,000 tons)	Acres[a] (1,000,000 acres)	Crop Index[b]
TVA	11.4 (8.4–18.0)	6.1 (5.1–18.0)	5.6 (4.2–7.9)		
Hee	15.8 (14.8–16.8)	7.9 (7.6–8.2)	7.1 (6.6–7.5)		
Ibach	13.0 (3.5–21.0)	6.9 (2.3–10.3)	8.4 (2.4–13.3)	300 (450–230)	150 (100–200)
Coleman	12.7	7.6	6.3		
1968–1969 (Actual)	5.9	3.9	3.3	334	112

SOURCES: John R. Douglas, Jr., "Changes in U.S. Plant Nutrient Use," *Changes in Fertilizer Distribution and Marketing*, Tennessee Valley Authority, Muscle Shoals, Alabama, 1965.

O. Hee, *A Statistical Analysis of U.S. Demand for Phosphate Rock, Potash, and Nitrogen*, Inform. Circ. 8418, U.S. Dept. Interior, Bur. of Mines, 1969.

D. B. Ibach, *Fertilizer Use in the United States*, Agr. Econ. Rpt. No. 92, USDA, May, 1966. "Consumption of Commercial Fertilizers in the United States," SpCr. 7 (10–70); Statis. Report Serv., USDA, Oct. 27, 1970.

R. Coleman, "The Outlook for Fertilizer," *Chemical Engineering Progress*, Vol. 64, No. 7, July, 1968, pp. 68–71.

[a] Median (range) predictions.

[b] Yield projection relative to 1960–1964 yield (base index = 100).

The unsolved problems reside in the technologies required to increase the fraction of nutrients harvested in crops and retained on the cropped land. Escaping nutrients, primarily nitrogen and phosphorus transferred to ground and surface water, upset the natural balance of plant growth and present a potential health hazard. Pollution is greatly affected by a number of variables; although it must be taken very seriously, pollution control moves basically on a collision course with food production. For example, Verdun (1970) and Nelson (1972) refer to nitrogen and phosphorus in the waters as the two prime plant nutrients that tend to regulate the growth of aquatic plants and therefore the eutrophication of inland waters. What is good for the soil and the dinner table becomes pollution when nutrients leave the area of application. The recent active attention focused on the potential harm of nutrient enrichment in streams and waterways arising from high levels of fertilizer application and subsequent runoff, leakage and soil erosion, is indicated by such papers as Biggar and Corey, 1969; Black, 1970; Garman, 1970; Goldberg, 1970; Martin *et al.*, 1970; Stanford *et al.*, 1970; Verdun, 1970; Viets, 1970; Nelson, 1972.

In addition to mounting concern over eutrophication, attention turned to the nitrate levels in the water consumed by humans and livestock.

This problem is particularly acute because of the concern in some localities that nitrates endanger the health of infants. Kearney *et al.* (1970) summarize the sources of nitrate in inland waters as nitrogen fertilizer, naturally occurring accumulations, sewage, livestock corrals, and industry.

The abundant use of phosphate detergents for household and industrial purposes has intensified concern over phosphate levels in water. Wadleigh estimated that, in 1968, two pounds of phosphate enter the sewage and thence the surface water per person-year. As indicated earlier, about 4½ million tons of phosphate was applied to United States soils as P_2O_5 in 1970. It has been estimated that practically all of the fertilizer phosophorus is absorbed by the mineral soil particles on the land and remains on the land, unless transported as sediment or in surface water. Allison (1966), Garman (1970), Black (1970) and Welch *et al.* (1971) present lysimeter data to show that only infinitesimal amounts of phosphate move through the soil in the soluble state.

In an effort to clarify the divergent views among agricultural spokesmen on the contribution of fertilizer nutrients to pollution, Frink (1969, 1971) considered United States land-management practices and land characteristics *vis-à-vis* three broad soil categories. The data, by soil classes, are indicated in Figure 3: Soils of low native fertility (types 1–5), which are highly leached, were compared to the soils of high native fertility (6–12), which are subject to much less leaching, and also to soils in arid regions (13–16), which are often low in fertility and subject to much less runoff.

Agriculture on soil types 1–5, primarily in the humid East and some areas of the West (see Figure 3) operates essentially on a "put and take" basis—that is, nutrients removed in crops must be applied each year as fertilizer. In this region rainfall is high, cropping is intensive, nitrogen and phosphorus added to the soil are lost by leaching and erosion. Kemper (1970) indicates that excess nitrogen applied to bare or frozen soil will be lost to the atmosphere by denitrification when the temperature rises, or will enter the groundwater. The loss of phosphorus through erosion not only poses a serious obstacle to maintaining an adequate nutrient supply but adds phosphorus to the surface waters.

Soil types 6–12 (plains and prairies) retain high residual fertility. The farmers in those areas are still mining the native soil nitrogen, and the soils deliver nitrate to groundwater even in the absence of additional fertilizer (Martin *et al.*, 1970; Goldberg, 1970). In many parts, severe erosion is providing high phosphorus in the waterways. Irrigation practices recycle some of the groundwater through the "soil–crop filter," thereby increasing the concentration of nitrate and other salts in the soil (Frink, 1971).

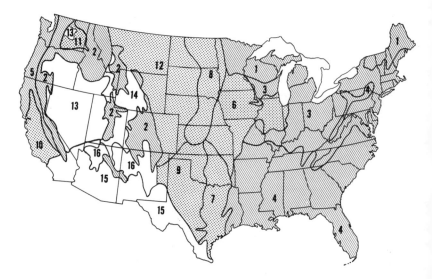

FIGURE 3   Generalized soils map of the United States. Soils 1–5 are generally highly leached and low in native fertility, while soils 6–12 are subject to less leaching and are high in native fertility. Soils 13–16 receive little water and are generally infertile (Frink, 1971).

Soil types 13–16 (primarily mountain and arid regions) are not under intensive agriculture because of the topography and because there is inadequate water for irrigation. In some of these areas, particularly in the West, nitrates may increase in the groundwater because they are subject to a closed irrigation system. Nitrates are less likely to increase in the eastern regions, where more water flows through the soil. Soil conservation measures will greatly reduce the amount of erosion and therefore loss of phosphorus, but will have little effect on the movement of nitrogen to groundwater (Kilmer, 1967).

Frink (1971) concluded that soils, climate and management practices differ so greatly from region to region of the United States that broad national generalizations concerning the contribution of fertilizers to water pollution are virtually worthless.

MEASUREMENTS OF NUTRIENT LOSS

Nutrient losses have been measured under a variety of agricultural practices in both fallow and cultivated land. Allison (1966), on review of the lysimeter data of several N^{15} experiments, concluded that rarely does a crop recover more than 50–60 percent of the nitrogen supplied as fertilizer. Leaching during the fall and early spring probably accounts for most of the loss (Stevenson and Wagner, 1970). The nutrient losses, though small on a percentage basis, may be sufficient to cause eutrophication (Viets, 1970). Taylor *et al.* (1971) have concluded that nutrient loss from agricultural watersheds, particularly of nitrogen and phosphorus, varies greatly and is markedly influenced by differences in fertilizer application. Therefore, Frink (1969) suggested that the assessment of nutrient loss in cultivated areas should be on a farming-system basis.

Forested watersheds in general are reported to lose less nitrogen and phosphorus than cultivated lands and the variation among soils and regions is generally reported as somewhat less. Bormann *et al.* (1968) reported a nitrogen loss of 1.6 lb/acre, whereas Frink found in 1967 that the loss was about 3 lb/acre of nitrogen and 0.22 lb/acre of phosphorus in a forested area of Connecticut. In a Potomac River basin, Jaworski and Hetling (1970) reported the losses at 1.4 lb/acre of nitrogen and 0.1 lb/acre of phosphorus, whereas Garman (1970) reported studies in 1968 in Minnesota showing losses (August to November) of about 3 lb/acre of nitrogen and about 0.12 lb/acre of phosphorus. (See also Cooper, 1969.) The effectiveness of growing plants in reducing the nutrient losses from soil was shown by Bormann *et al.* (1968). The removal of the forest cover was reported to result in a nitrogen loss of 50 lb/acre compared to a loss of less than 2 lb/acre on the forested soil. With phosphorus, the increased loss was about tenfold, totalling about 0.2 lb/acre.

Even in agricultural watersheds, considerable variation in nutrient loss has been reported. Jaworski and Hetling (1970) gave a loss per acre for nitrogen and phosphorus of 3.8 and 0.24 pounds, respectively, in the Potomac River watershed; whereas Biggar and Corey (1969) concluded from a study of published data that losses as high as 50 pounds and 20 pounds, for nitrogen and phosphorus, can occur. In Oregon, from the nutrients entering the Kilamath Lake, Miller and Tash (1967) concluded that 20 percent of the nitrogen and 25 percent of the phosphorus were from agricultural drainage; springs were also considered as an important source, accounting for 11 percent and 25 percent of the nitrogen and phosphorus lost.

FARMING SYSTEMS AND NUTRIENT LOSS

Corn is grown on 65 million acres of land and accounts for 40 percent of the nitrogen fertilizer used. Studies of nutrient use by corn as a function of the rate, method and time of application are therefore important. Lathwell *et al.* (1970) strongly favored adding nitrogen to corn as a summer side-dressing, both to increase the fraction used and to decrease environmental pollution. Their studies indicated that, the longer the fertilizer remained in the soil, the greater the probability of loss and of wash into the streams and groundwater. Thus, they strongly recommended that side-dressing be implemented.

Power (1970) related nitrogen loss to the amount of water. In arid areas, nitrogen loss was minimal when soils were not wetted below the plant root zone. However, when more nitrogen was added, or formed by nitrification, than was removed by the crop—and when rainfall was sufficient to percolate to a depth of 6 feet or more—the nitrogen moved below the rooting zone and eventually reached the groundwater.

In irrigated areas of California and along the Rio Grande, nitrogen loss and increases in groundwater level were correlated with the particular cropping practice. For example, with moderate-to-heavy fertilization, when truck garden products were planted and the water pumped from below—the nitrogen decreased. When celery was planted, the crop failed to use all of the nitrogen, and the nitrogen content of the soil increased from 42 ppm to 48 ppm. In three areas along the Rio Grande, Bower and Wilcox (1969) reported a wide variation in the renovation of irrigation water. They concluded that leached nitrogen near the water table was lost to the atmosphere following denitrification.

Examination of this data from United States farms indicates that practical systems can be devised to minimize the loss of nutrients to surface and underground waters. The data further emphasize the need for intensified agricultural research and education with the goal of devising crop management practices that minimize the loss of nutrients. Such studies, however, would have to be focused regionally or locally so that the results were applicable to given situations (Stevenson and Wagner, 1970; Pesek and Olson, 1970; Stanford et al., 1970).

Research and educational programs should also be focused on water quality. Since the prime uses of water go well beyond agriculture, the American people should know the main sources of pollutants, their extent, and how much it will cost in dollars and reduced yields to eliminate each of the pollution sources. Finally, research should be undertaken to develop agricultural production processing distribution systems that maximize benefits to society.

5

By-product Management

Management of the by-products of food production is one of the most difficult environmental problems facing food producers and processors. The Committee reviewed publications concerning management of animal waste, food processing waste, and sludge from municipal sewage disposal plants. The status of promising innovating approaches, federal and state regulatory actions, and developmental research in both the United States and Western Europe were reviewed.

The problems encountered in the management of animal waste, food processing waste, and sludge from municipal sewage disposal plants are similar. In each case, a large volume of material must be managed in a manner which disposes of a by-product while minimizing odors and nutrient leakage into streams and waterways. The material to be handled is primarily carbohydrate except in some food processing plants where management of lipid by-products are a problem.

The material cited in this report pertains primarily to management of animal waste. However, because of the similarity of the problems, many of the management principles will be applicable to the management of other types of food production by-products. In this report the Commit-

65

tee has drawn heavily from a recent review of Loehr (1971) in discussing alternatives for treatment and disposal of animal waste.

Increased overall requirements for agricultural products in recent years has been outstripped by the increase in demand for meat products. The most pronounced demand has been for beef and poultry products. An accompanying change has occurred in both the total number and size of meat-producing facilities. The trend toward larger units is expected to continue and to be accompanied by improved technical efficiency, with a smaller profit per animal processed and increased competition. Large-scale enclosed production units are also entering other phases of agriculture. The trend is virtually complete so far as small fowls, hens, broilers and ducks are concerned; it is increasing with swine (Muehling, 1967, 1969) and cattle (Loehr, 1969; Jedele and Andrew, 1972). The production of milk and eggs is also increasingly confined to this type of facility.

Current technology and manpower are inadequate to solve the new waste disposal problems generated by these large-scale production units. This is an especially difficult problem to resolve at a cost that is acceptable to the animal producer. The resulting impact on the environment, aesthetic values, public health, and stream and soil pollution will continue until a program of research and education is initiated to provide economically feasible waste disposal measures and the manpower to monitor and manage them.

The accumulated waste from beef and poultry feedlots alone constitutes a serious problem in terms of the astounding bulk and high nitrogen and carbohydrate content of the excrement. These pollutants contaminate atmosphere, water and land to varying degrees. The net effect depends largely on the population and the climate, particularly on the availability of water. To be effective, waste treatment and disposal methods must be inexpensive in dollars and labor, sharply reduce nuisances such as odor, and protect public health by improving sanitation. The serious inadequacies in animal waste treatment technology in the United States is particularly noticeable, for example, in the poultry producing regions of New England and of the Northeast, and on animal feed lots in the Midwest. In the densely settled, high moisture areas of the Northeast and the northern Midwest, unpleasant odors frequently generate major controversies. In the dry, more sparsely settled regions of the Southwest, the more significant aspect is the sheer accumulation of animal waste from the very large facilities. The public concern over this situation is due partly to odor but also to fear of health hazards. Furthermore, the educational facilities required to build the manpower pool needed to devise and implement effective methods for low cost disposal of large quantities of solid waste are lacking, though much in need of attention.

ENVIRONMENTAL EFFECTS

The nature and the magnitude of insults to the environment from animal waste generated in large-scale production units are outlined in several reviews (Anon., 1968; Loehr, 1968, 1972; Wadleigh, 1968; Freeman and Bennett, 1969; Miner and Willrich, 1970; Miner, 1971). The major adverse effects of the intensified agricultural practices in confinement production facilities stem from the accumulation of high nutrient waste, its transfer to the land for disposal, and through leaching its uncontrolled discharge into lakes, rivers and streams. The intensity of nuisance effect—primarily from odors—varies with moisture, rainfall, prevailing winds and population density. Surface runoff from cattle feedlots, manured land and waste-disposal lagoons can exceed the nutrient-handling capacity, in both surface and groundwaters, and unbalance the natural ecological systems. Excessive nutrient loads, especially nitrogen and phosphorus, promote stream eutrophication and endanger animal and human health; this excess of organic matter leads to the abundant growth of microorganisms and thus to a depletion of the supply of dissolved oxygen, which kills fish and causes pronounced odors. The odors, which are inevitable near production facilities and during distribution on land, represent a significant problem. Improved sanitation at confined production units, the installation of treatment facilities, and odor control or eradication, are sorely needed. With present technology they are both difficult and prohibitively expensive. In part, the increase in the animal and human population—especially as concentrated in certain regions—produces a waste load that exceeds the capacity of natural cycling processes. The human waste problem has grown more slowly; the effluent contains a lower concentration of organic material by a factor of nearly 100; and costs for treatment far in excess of those presently acceptable by the animal-production facilities are regarded as a normal community living expense.

The total United States agricultural–environmental conflict picture is as yet unclear. This is especially true in terms of the harmful effects of agricultural practices, such as applying nutrients to soil or disposing of waste from confined production units, as related to other domestic and industrial waste. Current information is far from definitive because data are limited and technology is changing rapidly. But, given these reservations, agriculturally derived pollution appears significant, especially on a regional and local level.

Water Quality

Examples of surface and groundwater deterioration, both due to animal waste, have been reported. The public concern with surface waters centers on nitrogen, usually as nitrate, and fish kills. Though there are few adequate monitoring systems, groundwater also appears most likely to deteriorate as a result of nitrogen, which percolates below the root zone. Data from both Missouri and Illinois indicate frequent—and in some cases excessive—nitrate levels beneath feedlots either in past or current use. Several reports indicate that the rural water supplies contain sufficient nitrate to be of concern in raising young livestock.

Agricultural wastes in surface water are not considered a major problem; nevertheless, increases of wastes above acceptable levels and examples of severe pollution as evidenced by fish kill have been reported. In the latter case, from a fiftieth to a fifth of the total fish kill in different years has been attributed to pollution of agricultural origin. Monitoring and increased effort at control, already evident in some areas, must be increased. Loehr (1968) reported an escalation in fish kill from agriculturally derived stream pollution of from 8 to 12 to 16 percent—in the years 1964, 1965 and 1967 respectively—with a drop in 1968 to less than 2.5 percent. Of the reported 422,000 fish killed in 1968, only 35,300 were attributed to manure-silage drainage.

Nitrate-nitrogen levels below certain feedlots were reported to run as high as 2000–4000 lb/acre as compared to standard soil levels of 50–150 lb/acre (Smith, 1967). Smith also reports that nitrate pollution persisted in some cases after land was no longer used as animal feedlots and that half to three fourths of the rural water supplies in Missouri contained nitrate at "levels to cause concern." Dickey et al. (1972) reported similarly high levels in Illinois, although not all were attributable to drainage from current or past animal-holding sites.

After excessive quantities of manure were applied to cropland, nitrate migrated through the soil in high concentrations (Witzel et al., 1969) and showed similar patterns of movement below irrigated and fertilized soils and below feedlots.

At present, groundwater pollution from agricultural waste is, for the most part, below the levels considered serious. The number of documented occurrences of groundwater pollution by agricultural wastes, however, continues to grow (White and Sunada, 1966; Stewart et al., 1967; Walker, 1969). Before establishing agricultural operations or choosing sites for land dispersal of wastes, the possibility of groundwater pollution should receive thorough investigation.

Runoff

Where animals are housed in the open—such as on cattle feedlots and duck farms—and where waste disposal on land has not been wisely executed, runoff can be a serious cause of local pollution. The danger is materially reduced in units where animals are completely housed, as in the case of most poultry and many hog and dairy operations.

The variability of rural rainfall–runoff interactions make actual documentation hard to secure. For example, Miner *et al.* (1966) recorded high concentrations of bacteria normally considered indicative of sanitary quality in feedlot runoff. The greatest concentrations were observed during warm weather, in periods of low rainfall, and when water soaking had solubilized the manure. Additional published accounts of investigations of runoff characteristics from feedlots and from manured fields include FWPCA, 1968; Owens and Griffin, 1968; Hensler *et al.*, 1969; Minshall *et al.*, 1969; Norton and Hansen, 1969; Loehr, 1970; Madden and Dornbush, 1971. Specific recommendations include the use of control measures that minimize the quantity of runoff that reaches surface waters.

Public Health

The list of infectious disease organisms common to man and other animals is lengthy, including the number that are waterborne (Decker and Steele, 1966). Drainage or runoff from animal production units that is permitted to reach a watercourse is a potential avenue for the spread of disease.

The effectiveness of soil for removing coliform and enterococcus bacteria from animal wastes is reported by McCoy (1969). Both adsorption during soil percolation and die-off (the latter, in part because of the inability of these bacteria to compete with the established soil microflora) are considered efficient—more than 98 percent being removed in the first 14 inches of soil. Concern over health is, therefore, minimal if percolation rather than runoff of raw sewage is involved, and the hazard decreases rapidly with distance from the site on which manure is added and incorporated by tilling.

The survival time of bacteria in feedlots can be important to public health. For example, McCalla and Elliott (1971) found that *Salmonella* and *Escherichia coli* do die rapidly under aerobic conditions and on feedlots. *Leptospira* have been reported to survive as long as 18 days in aerated beef manure (Diesch *et al.*, 1971).

MANAGEMENT

The use or recycling and the disposal of animal wastes constitute problems of great diversity—especially in the light of variations in the environment and other constraints. No single treatment has, therefore, been devised that is adequate for handling all agricultural production operations. All treatments in current use point toward final disposal of part or all of farm-animal wastes on the soil. The amount of water, of organic matter and of salt in the final residue are critical. As noted earlier in this section, agricultural by-product management is concerned primarily with recycling and otherwise reducing the amount and concentration of organic matter in the environment below levels that will upset the natural ecological conditions by surpassing the capacity of nutrient recycling processes. Primary attention has been focused on nitrogen and phosphorus. The two primary concerns are human health hazards and the avoidance of excessive oxygen depletion in water. The latter situation is directly deleterious to aquatic life and generates odor as an outcome of the anaerobic decomposition of animal excrement. The remedy replacement of oxygen in fluids of high organic matter concentration is very costly in terms of the energy required to mix and dissolve such a sparingly soluble gas into aqueous solutions.

The following brief general treatment of land disposal and odor control applies to all treatment and disposal systems as discussed immediately thereafter.

Land Disposal

Animal wastes can be valuable when added to soil, both as soil conditioners, and as plant nutrients. For maximal retention, these wastes would be incorporated into the soil as soon as possible after spreading. Bartlett and Marriott (1971) have discussed the subsurface injection of manure by mechanical equipment as a way of eliminating odor and minimizing runoff. These techniques do show some promise. The maximum level of application is governed by the capacity of the soil to prevent groundwater pollution and build-up of toxic materials. Braids (1972) has discussed land application of wastes as an essential step in nutrient recovery, the primary deterent being the cost of labor required relative to the value of nutrients recovered. Land dispersal represents the least expensive method now available, but abundant opportunity for innovation remains.

Odor Control

The troublesome odors from decomposition of organic material, including animal wastes, are due primarily to the activity of anaerobic bacteria. Access to oxygen to achieve complete, or nearly complete, oxidation of intermediate compounds is ultimately required. During anaerobic decomposition, much of the nitrogen of animal wastes is released as ammonia. In aerobic decomposition, part of the ammonia will escape into the atmosphere; that retained in the soil will undergo oxidation to nitrates, and improvement *vis-à-vis* plant growth and the reduction of odor.

A number of anaerobic holding procedures have been used with agricultural wastes. These will be discussed in detail under treatment and disposal, particularly in-house holding methods. Several procedures have been introduced to solve the ultimate problem, aeration. Mechanical surface aeration using rotors, floating aerators, oxidation ditches and aerated lagoons have been described (see Loehr *et al.*, 1971; Pos *et al.*, 1971, with respect to poultry excrement; Muehling, 1969, and Windt *et al.*, 1971, for swine; and Larson and Moore, 1971, for beef cattle). Jones *et al.* (1970) have published design and operation directions that have been applied successfully in reducing and controlling odors from animal waste. Converse *et al.* (1971) have studied the minimum amount of aeration required to prevent odor production under laboratory conditions; to date, applications to field conditions have not been reported. Foaming presents a problem during aeration with any material having high organic content. Anti-foaming agents, in general, are effective, but too expensive to use in agricultural treatment procedures.

Chemical modification of animal waste and the use of proprietary chemicals have been employed to prevent, suppress or mask odors. Of the chemicals recommended, hydrated lime and chlorine have been most successfully applied, especially to reduce the amount of hydrogen sulfide, ammonia and methane formed (Yushok and Bear, 1948; Deibel, 1967; Hammond *et al.*, 1968). Potassium permanganate has been employed on feedlots to control odors (Faith, 1964). Burnett and Dondero (1968) compared 44 commercial masking agents, counteractants and deodorants and recommended masking agents and counteractants as the most effective means of odor control. However, no completely effective agent emerged from this study.

Soil filtration has been examined as a way of removing gases. For example, Burnett and Sobel (1968) showed that ammonia up to 200 mg/liter, and hydrogen sulfide as high as 20 mg/liter, could be removed;

Gumerman and Carlson (1969) reported the removal of as much as 775 mg/liter of methyl mercaptan. Removal rates depend markedly on soil characteristics, temperature, moisture, on climate and on depth of soil. Depths ranging from 6 in. to 4 ft have been examined and shown to be effective. No single answer can be given. In one estimate, approximately one cubic foot of soil per ten chickens is considered sufficient to remove the odorous compounds from the effluent air of commercial poultry houses.

TREATMENT AND DISPOSAL SYSTEMS

The treatment methods and handling systems used to dispose of animal waste have been discussed in numerous symposia and widely reviewed (American Society of Agricultural Engineers, 1966, 1971; Anon., 1969, 1972; Muehling, 1969; Jones *et al.*, 1970; Miner, 1971). They constitute the main issues faced in agricultural by-product management and can be summarized as follows: (1) water flush methods, aerobic or anaerobic; (2) in-house holding procedures; (3) separation procedures; and (4) by-product recycling.

Though the high organic and nitrogen content (greater than 10 percent) of animal wastes would seem to justify their consideration as a natural resource, the cost of recycling compared with sale value of the products has not yet been favorable. Prior to this time, operations were too scattered to permit economical collection of refuse for processing; some acceleration can be expected now that large quantities of fecal and slaughterhouse waste accumulates in the vicinity of large industrial, enclosed facilities. In a later section on utilization of agricultural wastes, some initial steps will be mentioned.

The specific treatment–disposal processes found most effective to date for animal wastes from enclosed confinement production operations, are shown in Figure 4, Systems 1–9. Each system has advantages and limitations in specific environments and with certain wastes.

Water Flushing and Land Dispersal (Systems 1–3)

Since animal wastes are defecated in semisolid form, there is logic in direct treatment and disposal. Utitizing water in a flushing procedure introduces two problems, increased waste volume and handling of polluted water. Flushing methods are still employed in animal-production units, principally because of the limitations of more suitable procedures. Primitive, unreliable equipment that is scarce is a prime drawback with other methods. To this must be added the cost and scarcity of labor to

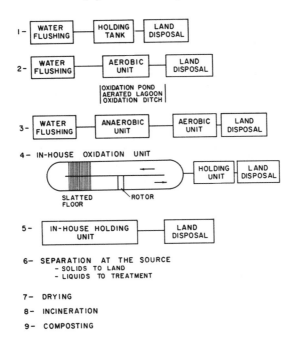

FIGURE 4 Systems for treating wastes from enclosed confined animal production operations (Loehr, 1971).

handle semisolid waste, which further encourage reliance on the more familiar procedure of water flushing.

The three flushing systems for animal waste disposal most commonly used today terminate in dispersal of both the effluent and the solid residue on the land. Since the effluent water is not of an acceptable quality to discharge into streams, runoff following dispersal on land must be avoided. For example, the waste may have to be applied below the surface or plowed into the soil as soon as feasible. If land disposal is not possible as a terminal step, a very high degree of organic matter removal is required before flushing water can be discharged into streams.

System 1: Direct Land Disposal + Holding Tank Many dairy operations utilize daily disposal of the animal and bedding wastes without a tank. Holding tanks, however, provide valuable flexibility; for example, they are useful when the waste cannot be dispersed directly on the land because crops are being grown there or the soil is too wet. Land dispersal has the advantages of simplicity and low cost. It is also the method traditionally accepted by the agricultural community. (This is more often the case in sparsely settled than in populated areas and those near urban communities.) If a holding tank is used in northern climates, the capacity should be sufficient for 3- to 5-month residue. Since the holding tanks now available are nonaerated, odoriferous compounds (including gases) will result from anaerobic decomposition—an annoying drawback. The odors prove most troublesome at times when the tank contents are mixed and pumped to transfer vehicles, and during dispersal on the land.

System 2: Aerobic Holding Tanks   The substitution of aerobic holding tanks for the anaerobic tank minimizes odor, often nearly eliminating it. An added advantage is the decrease in organic content. A drawback is that aerobic systems require a larger area, with an attendant higher cost. The aerobic lagoon incurs a continuous cost for power to run the mechanical aerator. The solid content of animal wastes is generally very high, and may be incompatible with a small unit. Still further, even after aerobic treatment the effluent may retain an appreciable biological oxygen demand (BOD), necessitating land disposal rather than direct discharge into receiving streams.

System 3: Anaerobic Surge + Aerobic Holding   Comparative costs in power and space will dictate whether to use System 2 or System 3. In the latter, an anaerobic or surge tank may be employed in front of an aerobic unit to collect the heavier solids and sustain a first decomposition. This reduces the required size but does not obviate the need for an aerobic unit. The anaerobic unit is generally mixed only through gasification and at lengthy intervals, when the accumulation of solids necessitates their removal. These anaerobic units are uncontrolled units built for high biological loads, rather than controlled digesters of the kind used for municipal waste–water sludge. This more concentrated animal waste produces an effluent with very high BOD and a high nitrogen and solid content. This effluent must be further processed; thus the anaerobic unit is not a complete answer to water pollution for animal wastes. The aerobic unit that follows the anaerobic one is similar to those employed in System 2; the last step is land dispersal of the minimal residual solids.

In-house Holding Units (Systems 4 and 5)

Systems 4 and 5 are the aerobic and anaerobic in-house lagoon or oxidation ditch, respectively. They represent the counterparts of Systems 1–3 but do not employ water flushing and, therefore, require smaller areas.

They are rapidly gaining favor among the new alternatives for animal waste management suitable for confined animal production facilities.

System 4: In-house Oxidation   Three advantages accrue from the in-house oxidation ditch: (1) inexpensive construction, when designed and built as an integral part of the confinement building; (2) only the minimum odor inherent in an aerobic design; and (3) decreased labor and handling cost through incorporation of a slotted floor that permits the automatic removal of refuse to the ditch. More than 200 livestock oxidation ditches are now in operation—the majority for swine production.

A mechanical rotor is provided for aeration; a holding unit, generally also aerated, is available to capture the overflow prior to disposal on land. Evaporation during oxidation and from rotor action reduces overflow relative to input, with further decrease in eventual runoff. The detention time in an oxidation ditch is long, frequently a matter of months. Effluent quality is good but not suitable for discharge into surface water (because of a high residual BOD). The mechanical rotor can be operated more successfully if a constant liquid level can be maintained; if the holding tank is not aerated, the contents will become anaerobic and develop the high bacterial content and increased odor characteristic of many anaerobic disposal systems.

System 5: In-house Anaerobic Solids Accumulation   Dairy and poultry operations rather commonly employ undisturbed pits below the animals, where wastes are left to accumulate for periods that may be greater than a year. Upon removal, the odor can be severe. If the removal is restricted to periods when likelihood of complaints is least (that is, early in the spring or in late fall when the waste can be incorporated immediately into the soil), this system may be very adequate.

The advantages include a minimum of handling and waste volume. Excess water is not necessary, except occasionally at the time of removal. The labor and energy costs are minimal, because aeration is avoided, and little attention is needed between periods of removal. Because the system is concentrated and the quantity of accumulated waste material often underestimated, producers have encountered difficulties such as lacking adequate land for disposal and sufficient equipment for waste removal and transfer.

Liquid–Solids Separation (System 6)

This category is rather less a system than a combination of procedures. The liquid fraction of wash water from animal residue can be processed by System 1, 2 or 3—as can any liquids containing organic matter formed by leaching or by water flushing.

The solids removed from the liquid phase can either be subjected to treatment as solid waste (in line with System 7, 8 or 9) or utilized by recycling, as discussed later in this section. Waste disposal with less financial loss (sometimes even modest gain) and with less environmental insult is receiving increased attention.

Use-Disposal of Solid Waste (Systems 7, 8 and 9)

Additional schemes for disposal of high levels of solid organic waste are primarily aimed at nuisance removal. System 7 (*drying*) is the least complex; System 8 extends drying to *incineration;* and System 9 employs *composting,* a time-dependent biological reduction of organic matter by oxidation. Investigation has shown these three types of processes to be technically feasible in dealing with animal wastes. They are presently in wide use in one area or another. Both drying and composting imply a market for the product, which again may depend on special circumstances. There is some advantage in using animal manures as supplements during the composting of municipal wastes because of their high nitrogen and carbon content.

System 7: Drying Drying is the least expensive technique when performed by exposing the waste to air as a solid layer; however, it may require heat, depending on the weather, and therefore the expense of fuel.

System 8: Incineration Incineration is by far the most expensive technique for disposal of solid animal waste. Furthermore, burning does not constitute complete disposal, since 10–30 percent of the initial waste weight will remain as ash. The problem of ash disposal itself has not been completely solved.

System 9: Composting Composting is an extension of drying that includes the time needed for biological oxidation.

All the methods of handling solid waste disposal face the same odor and pollution control difficulties that attend procedures 1–5. Some investigators suggest that the solids disposal systems will become more prevalent and more necessary—perhaps even more economically feasible—as the size of animal production units increases, and that additional impetus may be received from societally imposed constraints on the quality of discharged waste water.

Unenclosed Production Systems (System 10)

Discussion thus far has focused on the trend toward confined, enclosed, and rather large animal-production units and on modified procedures for handling the housing and disposal of the animal wastes. The unenclosed systems characteristic of feedlots are designed for smaller numbers of animals, but are increasingly to be found in the South and Southwest where climate permits far larger numbers because of the larger available areas per animal and minimal runoff leaching. Open or non-enclosed systems are still widely used and are increasing in both size and number. High nitrogen content and the escape of nitrogen from the feedlots are critical factors in the unenclosed systems; in addition, runoff is most troublesome in many cases and contributes very markedly to pollution. Thus, runoff-retention ponds or lagoons are required as holding facilities for runoff from feedlots during and following rain. They are designed primarily as collection rather than treatment units (Gilbertson, 1970). These procedures have been shown to be effective in dry areas (e.g., in Kansas, Texas, Oklahoma and Colorado) and are in fact the preferred methods.

RECYCLING AND BY-PRODUCT DEVELOPMENT FOR ANIMAL WASTE

To consider agricultural wastes as a resource is in no sense new. Increased awareness derives from an overloading of natural systems and from the development of economically feasible systems for the disposal of plant and animal waste from very large, industrial, animal-production facilities. These concentrated facilities have been engendered primarily by increases in technology, a narrowing of economic margin for profit, and an increased concern with public health and environmental insult. Most of these last, in turn, derive from increases in human populations and increased food demands.

So long as production units were relatively small, the collection of by-products and their use for constructive and economically feasible purposes were not feasible with available technology. There are exceptions: For example, furfural—an important industrial intermediate for organic synthesis—has been prepared largely from oat husks obtained in large quantity at cereal processing plants or from corncobs and husks obtained from corn processing plants devoted principally to the production of corn sugar and corn oil. More recently, very large enclosed feedlots and contained units for poultry, swine and beef production have produced animal waste far in excess of what can be disposed of through municipal sewage plants. These plants have tended to appear in remote areas because of aesthetic and economic considerations, although there are some in densely populated areas as well. In this context, and in the context of plant by-product utilization, there are pressures for new ideas, new technologies and an improved economic base.

The primary need in agricultural by-product disposal is to reduce the pollution and health hazard involved. However, the push thus far has been economic—although not so much for an economically important product as for a reduction in the cost of disposal, which is reflected in the cost of the primary products and passed on to the consumer. Reduction of the public health hazard and insult to the environment, the aesthetics of odor control, and maintenance of the rural environment for recreation have been secondary—though highly visible—additional forces. Witness in this regard the pollution of the lakes and streams that renders them unavailable for recreation.

Many examples of waste utilization as a means of solving waste-management problems and improving the economic outlook have been cited (Heald and Loehr, 1971; USDA, 1971e). Many plant products—e.g., fruit and vegetable wastes—are utilized as stock feed. Tomato by-products from canning are dehydrated and used as animal feed. Similarly, corncobs and husks, and wastes from canning peas, corn and citrus fruits, are separated from the liquids and processed into dried cattle feed. Animal manure, after composting or drying, has been pelletized and used as soil conditioners, animal-feed supplements and as a fertilizer base. In special instances, for example, peach pits have been used for charcoal. A full account of the utilization of plant and animal by-products is as comprehensive as is their composition. The primary economic factors derive from the richness of the ingredients concerned, the cost of extracting them, and their unit value. Success in disposal is perhaps best exemplified by the utilization of horse manure via composting for commercial mushroom production, until the growth of the industry and a decreasing horse population led to a shortage of the needed raw material. The industry now uses molasses and alfalfa as a substitute organic base.

As environmental awareness increases, traditional disposal procedures such as burning—particularly to dispose of plants and diseases, weed seeds and insects—are becoming less acceptable. These procedures are increasingly being replaced, especially as the cost of chemical methods for control decrease relative to labor costs. Among the procedures used for by-product recycling are composting, development, drying and dehydrating, methane production and water reclamation—to be discussed in that order.

Composting

Composting provides an opportunity to recover and reuse a portion of the nutrients, as well as the organic fraction of agricultural wastes. Though animal wastes can be composted alone, they are frequently extended by combining them with wastes of high carbon–nitrogen ratio, such as sawdust, corncobs, paper and municipal refuse. Enthusiasm for composting in the United States has been based largely on the possibility of producing a saleable, potentially profitable, end product. Experience in this country, however, indicates that—except for special cases—composting should be thought of as a treatment process and not as a profit-making operation. Composting is but one component in an overall waste-management system.

Composting of poultry, beef, and dairy wastes with mechanical equipment has produced a suitable end product (Wiley, 1964; Livshutz, 1964). Onsite composting of poultry manure has been shown (Howes, 1966; Bell and Pos, 1970) to produce an odorless, fly-free environment at relatively low cost.

Solids from fruit processing, such as discarded whole fruit, halves and fragments that may or may not have been lye peeled, have been satisfactorily composted (Rose *et al.*, 1965). In this instance, separate peach and apricot wastes were mixed with municipal compost, rice hulls and other material; lime added to the mixture helped neutralize the fruit acids that were generated and accelerated the process.

Under ordinary circumstances, the cost of applying compost to the land exceeds the benefits received. Agricultural wastes can be stabilized by composting. The potential also exists for salvage and recycling of inorganic and organic resources in solid wastes. Their use as soil conditioning do not, however, make compost attractive to United States agriculture. A suitable market must be available before composting can be attractive as a method for the disposal of agricultural solid wastes. Without a suitable market, most of the original dry matter remains for further disposal.

By-product Development

The meat slaughtering and packing industry is one example of an industry that utilizes techniques that convert agricultural wastes into useful products. Typical by-product uses are tallow and grease from fats, animal feed from meat scraps, blood and feathers, pharmaceutical products from animal glands, and bone meal from bones.

The wastes from vegetables and fiber-processing plants have been intensively studied for many years for possible use as animal feeds, as a raw material for manufactured products, and as a source of chemical compounds.

The nature of food-processing plant operations rarely makes it economical to collect, process and utilize the solids contained in liquid wastes. The utilization of these wastes therefore hinges largely upon whether the usable fraction can be separated and collected from the water being discharged from a processing plant. The reusable material is present in this water as very dilute suspensions of highly variable composition such as peels, skins, pulp, seeds and fibers. The liquid fraction may be saline, alkaline or acidic and contains a large variety of soluble organic compounds. In some processing operations, where the separation is comparatively easy, an economical by-product may result. A notable example is the production of molasses and pulp from the processing of sugar cane and sugar beets. These by-products can be used as animal feed supplements. The greatest opportunity for by-product recovery exists when wastes are separated into specific fractions at the source.

In addition to the use of fruit- and vegetable-processing solids for animal feeds, animal wastes have been considered as a potential component of animal feeds, for they contain appreciable energy and nutritive value. The utilization of this energy offers yet another approach to the recycling of agricultural wastes for beneficial use. A number of studies have shown that manure from such ruminants as cattle can be incorporated into feed rations of other ruminants without adversely affecting animal growth or health (USDA, 1971e).

In general, the nutritive value of animal wastes incorporated into feed rations is greater if the wastes of monogastric animals are added to the feed ration of ruminants and if the ruminant wastes are treated chemically before being added to feed rations. The experimental use of animal wastes in feed rations is not restricted to the United States. Research on this topic has been reported from South Africa, Canada, Australia and England. The data indicate that, when sound nutritional principles are followed, a portion of animal wastes can be used as a feed supplement for animals. However, the extent of transmittal of drugs, feed additives and pesticides to the second animal and to agricultural products, such as eggs and milk, remains to be clarified.

It must be recognized that the use of processing waste in animal feed rations is not an ultimate disposal method since a portion of it is not utilized by the animal and will remain for disposal. Recycling of wastes in this manner cannot go on indefinitely. Wastes treated and disposed of

via animals constitutes a reduction, not an ultimate disposal; a completely closed loop cannot be accomplished via refed animal wastes.

Drying and Dehydration

These are not utilization processes as such, but are designed to fashion a
product that can be used as a soil conditioner or as a feed supplement.
Dried animal wastes are likely to have more sale value if they are pack-
aged and sold to the home gardener, florist or nurseryman. Dried animal wastes have a greater potential for utilization than do food-processing wastes because the animal wastes generally contain more nutrients. Both of these processes have the same end result, i.e., removal
of moisture and reduction of waste volume.

When heat is used to accelerate the drying process, temperatures in
the 93–593°C (200–1100°F) range have been used. These temperatures
will volatilize a number of the organic compounds present. The gaseous
effluent from the high-temperature drying can itself be a source of odors
and generate complaints; satisfactory after-burners or other air pollution control equipment may be necessary.

The market potential of dehydrated agricultural wastes is unknown.
Without a suitable market, drying of wastes will often be uneconomi-
cal. Low temperature, natural or forced-air drying of wastes can reduce
the volume of wastes to be handled and can perhaps be incorporated
into a feasible land-disposal, waste-management system.

Methane Production

During the anaerobic digestion of animal wastes, gases containing
60–80 percent methane can be produced if consistently high rates of
digestion are maintained. These gases have been considered as an usable
energy source if close to the site where they are generated. Gas can
be produced at the rate of approximately 8–9 cu ft/pound of volatile
solids added to the digester when poultry, beef cattle and hog wastes
are processed. Lower gas production rates result when sheep and dairy
cattle wastes are digested since much of these materials are no longer
biodegradable.

The controlled conditions, equipment and associated costs that are
essential for the success of this method are higher than for alternative
waste-management methods. Consequently, little if any usable gas is
actually produced and utilized from the anaerobic digestion of agricultural wastes, although the process remains a potential source of
future energy.

Water Reclamation

Agriculture is a major consumer of water in the United States, primarily for use in food processing and irrigation. Conversely, an important re-usable by-product of the food and fiber industry is water. These waters can be recycled in processing plants, irrigation systems, and to recharge groundwater.

Irrigation agriculture is changing. The quantity of water used in irriga-tion is better controlled, and efforts are being made to achieve maximum efficiency. The reuse of irrigation water can be accomplished with a return pumping system, whereby the normal and irrigated runoff is caught in shallow ponds and reapplied to other fields. The primary pur-pose of this method is to increase efficiency; a secondary outcome is that soluble and solid materials usually lost in runoff are kept on the land.

Land disposal of agricultural waste waters offers further possibilities for water reclamation. The microbial and plant action in the plant–soil filter removes objectionable organics, most inorganics, and bacteria. Upon reaching the groundwater level, the waste water has been renovated. Care must be taken under these circumstances to avoid the leaching of unacceptable concentrations of nitrates into groundwater.

Like land disposal of waste waters, applying manure to soils requires proper disposal rates to avoid developing saline soils and contaminated runoff and leachate. Through careful planning and control, spray irriga-tion of food-processing waste can be adapted to various ground condi-tions and terrain. This method has been used year-round, as well as for seasonal operations of food processing plants, in many states.

EUROPEAN ACTIVITIES

The approaches to agricultural by-product utilization in Europe are not drastically different from those currently in use or under development in the United States. The differences have been decreasing rather than in-creasing since World War II, when the economic situation resulting from increased industrialization in the European countries converged with that taking form in the United States. Two prime differences can be cited: The very large-scale animal-production facilities for poultry, swine and beef are primarily American, rather than western European, at this time; and many European countries import a larger fraction of their food products than does the United States and have a greater tendency to consider agricultural residues as food and fuel resources. Allred (1966) points out that manure is considered important in many European countries for the improvement of soil tilth and structure; the reduction of leaching, particularly from light-textured soils, and the slow release of nutrients are viewed as plus factors, as is the decrease in soil and water erosion.

European waste treatment procedures include oxidation ditches and liquid addition of digested manures after extended aerobic processes (Scheltinga, 1966). The solids are, in general, returned to the land. Damage has been reported only in Northern Ireland, where most of the stock feed is imported and the waste returned to the soil (McAllister, 1971). The damage to land by grazing animals has been attributed to high potassium concentrations (100–360 mg/liter of soil). International communication and exchange of information are effective, so that the dispersal of available information on new techniques and equipment is anticipated.

EDUCATION AND RESEARCH

New issues in by-product management are presented whenever agricultural practices change. As stated earlier, animal waste from feedlots and from enclosed, industrial-type, animal facilities cannot be disposed of within permissive cost levels by current technologies for municipal and industrial sewage systems. Thus, new skills, new research and new technologies must be developed. Possible markets for treated waste residues or new products should also be expanded. The relevant areas seem to be (1) technology transfer; (2) interdisciplinary research; and (3) education of additional personnel.

The problem–response sequence characteristic of the American system of individual initiative at times lacks sensitivity. Recent advances have served to emphasize how rapid are the response times required and how extensively nature is insulted before the response is initiated. An increasing need for longer range planning is accentuated by the accumulation of very large production units that overrun the natural resources of a given region before current technologies can respond. These changes have increased the hue and cry for technology transfer, interdisciplinary research, and the building of a manpower pool with a "more modern"– i.e., more effective–capability to meet developing problems.

If present practices continue, greater efficiency in food production is expected to continue and to result in increased amounts of agricultural waste on smaller acreages and in fewer locations. Disposal of these wastes in an economic and satisfactory manner will continue to challenge the talents of individuals in many disciplines. In the past, the management of agricultural waste focused primarily on subjecting specific products to specific treatments. This has resulted in the discovery of many beneficial and feasible processes. At present, however, the problem does not appear likely to be solved by simple extension of current technology. As a result, it would appear essential that new concepts, new types of research and education, and especially inter-disciplinary activities, will be required. It is suggested that these may derive from expertise in biological sciences, including the animal sciences, and from chemistry and engineering. The latter may extend beyond the current education and domains of agricultural, civil and sanitary engineering or may promote their movement into new territories. If so, an additional economic base will be needed for training new people and to attract established experts. The procedures may well impinge on both public and private law and may extend to land-use policy and environmental planning and design.

It has been suggested by some that educational institutions should re-orient both undergraduate and graduate educational programs toward solving the current and anticipated problems in environmental quality and agricultural waste management. Techniques to attract and educate personnel, with the specific object of building a pool of qualified man-power devoted to this area, is critical.

An educational program for the general public, the farmer, the agri-cultural specialist and the operators of larger scale agricultural enterprises is also needed. It must be devoted to more specific phases of production and processing to determine which methods would be most acceptable. Information must also be transmitted to the professional and technical individuals who are capable of solving problems in technology and of preparing the communities for the magnitude of the costs that will be incurred. Such techniques as workshops, symposia and extension pro-grams, may be required.

SUMMARY

Greater efficiency in food production will continue to occur, with the result that increased amounts of agricultural wastes will be produced on smaller acreage and in fewer locations. Methods to handle and dispose of these wastes in an economic and satisfactory manner will continue to challenge the talents of individuals in many disciplines.

Current and past agricultural waste management studies have primarily dealt with the treatment of specific agricultural wastes, using specific treatment or disposal processes. This approach has been beneficial in delineating the more feasible processes. However, we have reached the point where broader concepts, broader types of research and train-ing, especially interdisciplinary activities, are needed.

Solutions to problems in this area will not originate with individuals working in a single discipline. Coordinated, multidisciplinary activities are necessary. Important disciplines include sanitary engineering, agricultural engineering, agronomy, economics, and animal science. Such multidisciplinary activities should include all aspects of the animal production operation, including interactions between feed, animal housing, waste production, handling techniques, treatment, disposal and reuse. Studies that look only at treatment or only at disposal consider only part of the problem. Studies of the overall production scheme can contribute to more realistic solutions as tradeoffs within the operation may be possible.

To date, little attention has been given to the definition of agricultural waste-management areas that are most likely to benefit from accelerated effort or to investigations of tradeoffs between foreseeable technical improvements and their effect on environmental quality. Increased emphasis and support should be given to studies that look at and develop total waste-management systems that are consistent with animal production and food processing systems. To date, the major emphasis has been on the treatment and disposal aspects.

The land is and will remain an acceptable disposal point for treated and untreated animal wastes under good crop- or land-management practices. However, additional information is needed to define these practices clearly when they are used in connection with waste disposal. To carry out these measures requires knowledge of the fate of organic and inorganic constituents to avoid secondary pollution caused by runoff or soil–water percolation to groundwater or such a high accumulation of salts that the soil is rendered unfit for production. Investigations are needed to determine the capacity of soil to accept wastes (including its limitations in this regard) and to delineate the degree of waste treatment that may be appropriate prior to land disposal.

Studies on the effects of adding large quantities of farm-animal wastes and other by-products to the soil should be expanded. Particular emphasis should be given to exploring areas of possible conflict with food production, and to loss of nutrients to streams.

Because the land is the logical disposal point for animal wastes, prior treatment of the wastes need only be compatible with that necessary to achieve satisfactory land disposal. Waste management is more flexible when land disposal is practiced. High treatment efficiencies prior to land disposal may not be necessary, as these are not needed when land disposal is the final step.

Considerable research has been conducted to delineate the characteristics of animal wastes and the fundamentals of treating these wastes.

The more promising approaches are now becoming clearer and additional research of this nature is needed. However, projects that will demonstrate feasible treatment processes are urgently needed.

A number of demonstration projects showing specific animal operations are needed to consider the effect of variations in season, geography, management, and size on the feasibility and effectiveness of the different waste-management systems and to assess adequately the costs of specific systems. Skepticism and conservatism customarily greet new or different treatment systems; demonstration projects speed the adoption of a successful approach.

Support for research and demonstration should come primarily from two general sources: agencies concerned with maintenance of environmental quality and responsible for its enforcement, and agencies that understand agricultural production and can assist in the integration of proper waste-management methods with production procedures.

Efforts are needed to develop methods that utilize any new wastes from agricultural production. All activities in this direction must be directed toward effective and economically feasible solutions. One aspect of all these solutions should be the development of adequate markets for the usable by-products; in the absence of an adequate market, the recovered material is of little value.

Overall investigations should be made of the economic impact of agricultural waste management and agricultural production. The size of agricultural operations is continually increasing, creating the potential for environmental difficulties. In one sense, this benefits the public, since food prices are held down by the economies of greater efficiency. At some point, however, the size of the operations may cost the public more in terms of the environment than is worth the benefits derived. Does such a point occur and if so, when? Other interesting points that deserve evaluation include the social benefits and the actual costs of environmental control of agricultural activities and their distribution.

Technical solutions to the utilization of agricultural wastes exist; and others will be found. The application of these methods will depend upon development in the social, legal, economic, political, and in the marketing and public relations areas. The agricultural waste utilization method most effective for the vast quantity of agricultural wastes continues to be land disposal in a crop-production cycle, with or without prior treatment of the wastes.

6

Other Aspects of
Food and Fiber
Production

PRODUCTS FOR AGRICULTURE

Agriculture consumes only a small portion of the lumber produced in America. H. R. Josephson (1970), Director of Forest Economics and Marketing Research, USDA, estimates that, of the timber products consumed in 1970, around 2 percent was used on farms, chiefly in the form of lumber. Thus, routine inaccuracies in projections of American lumber consumption will be greater than the total amount demanded by agriculture!

Josephson's estimate can be reconstructed from "Timber Trends in the U.S.," USDA Forest Resource Report No. 17 (February, 1965). Projections show little change in demand for lumber and some increase for plywood. Agriculture's annual lumber demand is expected to be about 2 billion board feet until the end of the century, while plywood demand grows to 300–600 million sq ft (calculated on the basis of a 3/8-in. sheet). The demand for posts by all users will be steady near 100 million cu ft/yr; agriculture's demand for poles is a small fraction of the American total of 100 million cu ft/yr. The total of these is about 0.3 billion cu ft/yr.

These projections must now be related to America's total consumption. This is expected to rise from 13 billion cu ft in 1970, to 15 in

87

1980, and 21 in 2000. Domestic production met 87 percent of this demand in 1970. Softwoods constitute 71 percent of the consumption. Thus agricultural consumption of forest products is negligible.

Forests occupy a third, or 759 million acres, of the 50 states. Of this area, 509 million acres are commercial forest. Surprisingly, 2/3 of the commercial forest is east of Colorado, and commercial forests increased by 24 and 8 million acres, respectively, in the two decades just past.

During the remaining years of this century, anticipated harvest will reduce the inventory of standing timber, even if the forest area remains large. Some of this reduction of inventory is not to be regarded as unfortunate, however, because it will merely liquidate old stands having little net growth. Nevertheless, without major changes in technology, timber growth, or land use, the cut of timber will exceed net growth considerably by the end of the century. Demands for land for other uses could enlarge this deficit, while more nearly complete utilization and improved management of the growing trees could bring the situation more nearly into balance.

FUTURE TECHNOLOGY

By extrapolating national needs to a given time and then dividing by a given yield per acre, the number of acres required to feed and clothe the United States population can be predicted for the years ahead. The value of the prediction depends, of course, on the validity of the assumptions, and the sands of years past are littered by the bones of ridiculous prophesies rendered invalid by technological changes. Careful examination of the changes in demands and yields through recent decades—especially the rates of acceleration or deceleration of change—should, however, improve the accuracy of the prediction.

One of the happiest outcomes of technology is seen in the relation between time and corn yield. This curve shows an average rise from 40 bushels of corn per acre in 1950 to double that in 1970. It would seem that one has only to project this to the end of the century to be confident that very little land and very few farmers can produce all the food required by the United States population; however, two things can go wrong with this simple and optimistic extrapolation: First, some curves relating output to input in agriculture are beginning to level off; second, the goals of technology may shift from increasing yields to improving environmental quality, slowing the rise in yield per acre.

C. R. Frink (personal communication, 1971) of the Connecticut Agricultural Experiment Station has found that many of the indicators of increasing yield are no longer rising as rapidly as they once were: The index of agriculture output per unit of input, for example, rose from 85 to 110 between 1950 and 1963 but has been steady since that time. In addition, the brief spectacular increase in persons supplied per farm worker that occurred in the mid-1960's is essentially over, and the crop acreage per person is no longer declining as rapidly as it did in the 1950's. Food prices have been climbing rapidly since the mid-1960's. The corn yield is no longer increasing rapidly with the increased use of plant nutrients. Yields of wheat, rye, rice, cotton, sugar beets, cotton seed and peanuts appear to be leveling off. The yield of potatoes is leveling off. The number of eggs per hen appears to have reached a maximum, while the rate of increase of milk per cow may be declining slightly. The feed consumed per 100 pounds of production is decreasing for broilers; while milk, hogs, cattle and calves and sheep and lambs actually require more concentrated feed per unit of production now than they did in the past. Thus, the ever-increasing productivity of agriculture cannot be relied upon.

There is, of course, another reason to suspect that agriculture yields may not increase as rapidly in the future as in the past. In short, the goals of technology must shift—or at least will shift—from increasing yields to improving environmental quality. Consider the use of fertilizers and pesticides. Many of the spectacular increases of the past have been the result of the increased consumption of these two classes of chemicals; but, if the leakage of these materials beyond the farmer's field requires that he use less of them, yields cannot go on increasing in this fashion. Further, if the goals of the researcher become—as they likely will—such things as safety in insect control and in nonpolluting modes of fertilizer application, the increases in yield are bound to slow. To draw a very simple analogy, if one is building an automobile for safety rather than speed, it is virtually certain to go more slowly than will the automobile built for the single-minded speed enthusiast.

THE RURAL ENVIRONMENT

7

A Livable Countryside

The problems of maintaining and enhancing the quality of rural living, coupled to the problems of food and fiber production and of recreational needs of the whole society, have been addressed by the Committee in various combinations. In some instances, attention to the feasibility of environmental planning—especially of enforcement—in the present climate of American society has identified areas in need-of future research and decision making.

Recurring questions needing resolution on a regional and national scale include: Is the quality of rural life optimal or merely acceptable? Is it adaptable to present or future needs, or is it static? Have the "good old days" been over-idealized, or were they in part realistic? What is the likely degree and rate of change? What adaptations are possible? What should be the limiting factors, in addition to economic feasibility? Shall the changes be on a free-enterprise basis or subject to societal modifications? If some measure of the latter is to prevail, how shall it be applied, and when?

The documentation, format and mode of presentation in this chapter have been principally those of the Subcommittee on Environmental Design, working with the Subcommittee on Resource Allocation. The recommendations in Chapter II embody the main features that were identified by the entire Committee as deserving concern, study and action. It is no longer clear that certain attempts to enrich the life of the food and fiber producer and his family, and to improve the facilities for recreation and living for the part-time resident, will not lead to urbanization and the consequent decay of the very amenities that are thought to characterize rural America. What is envisioned as the overall need for financial, cultural and intellectual changes may foster future urban sprawl. Nor does the fact that the fragile land is essential to certain aspects of production and maintenance any longer guarantee that it will not suffer. It even seems likely that the natural resources of rural areas may be diverted to support the effort of highest yield from land, water and labor.

Problems have been identified in three time scales: (1) short-range problems that can be attacked on the basis of available data; (2) those of intermediate range (2–5 years) identifiable by agricultural, environmental design, and economics experts from available data, but in need of selection and application; (3) long-range research needs, looking to population and societal conditions in the next decade or two.

THE PROBLEM

Several trends identifiable in the United States—and, in a broader sense, in the world at large—have occurred since the Industrial Revolution of the nineteenth century. Massive migration to cities from rural areas (a worldwide phenomenon) has been one. This population movement and the resulting change in pattern of human settlement has been accelerated in the United States by intensified capitalization of agriculture. Continued increase in the efficiency of food and fiber production has resulted in a greatly reduced demand for unskilled labor in rural areas.

Programs to encourage growth in rural areas have been developed by several departments of the national government. Some of these programs, especially those of USDA, are designed primarily to improve the quality of rural life. The Department of the Interior has collaborated with USDA for many years in areas dealing with wind erosion, water erosion, soil conservation, etc.

The Secretary of Agriculture's report in 1969 (USDA, 1970a) outlined many ongoing programs and mentioned several new ones that the Rural Affairs Council, then recently created, might recommend. The programs discussed in the report under "Creating Opportunity in Rural America" and "Resource Management and Conservation"—if applied with adequate imagination and initiative in collaboration with the Department of the Interior—should provide a framework for innovation.

Under the "Role of Research" in the Secretary's report, broad areas of study directly bearing on the social, aesthetic, or synergetic aspects of the many separate rural studies were discussed. The cost–benefit equilibrium of "goods" and "bads" included social and aesthetic values, as well as economic ones. The 1969 report referred to a "Massive Two-Pronged Attack . . . to improve materially the economic and social attractiveness of rural areas" and "the effective upgrading of the educational and working skills of the labor force."

The Committee on Agriculture and the Environment recommends a continuation and expansion of the approach utilizing the Cooperative Extension Service as a tool for rural development. The Cooperative Extension Service in each state should work with state committees for rural development to coordinate existing programs and recommend new ones. Committees for rural development in each state have been given expanded responsibilities through Cooperative Extension, including that of "conducting innovative rural development projects." These offer more hope for realization than comparable efforts in cities because there is a tradition of federal–state cooperation in agriculture.

STRATEGIES FOR IMPROVEMENT

Assuming it is desirable to attract large numbers of people out of metropolitan areas and back to rural America, two kinds of programs are needed:

1. Programs aimed at radically raising the level of services available to the rural population, thus reducing the large and often growing gap between rural and urban services. Accomplishing this will require a refocusing of national priorities and a determination to improve life in rural America. Both the reach and the funding of existing programs will have to be expanded, and their urban bias eliminated. Such programs must be streamlined to take full advantage of recent advances in technology and to respond to changes in service demands and to capitalize new methods for delivering services.

2. Programs to direct rural settlement into logical patterns on the land. Most rural areas are limited in the number of people the local resources can support. Uncontrolled in-migration could destroy the natural and cultural amenities; careful planning is, therefore, necessary. In many situations, additional information is needed.

The Advisory Commission on Intergovernmental Relations (1968) carefully examined the implications of such a policy in the report entitled *Urban and Rural America: Policies for Future Growth*. It concluded that governmental programs constitute significant forces toward urbanization and economic growth, and that a national policy to deal with urban growth is needed.

Developing technologies offer promise of revitalizing nonmetropolitan communities. Although job opportunities will be the key factor in determining whether this promise is realized, the Committee on Agriculture and the Environment believes that the availability of decent housing and top-quality educational and medical services will be very important, and that a massive program to develop systems for their delivery is essential.

Simply attracting people to move back to rural America is not enough. Such a movement must be carefully structured if it is to attain three basic goals: (1) Preserve those amenities in the rural environment that will attract people; (2) maintain a diversity of choice as to settlement size, location and character; and (3) safeguard land resources for the agricultural and recreational needs.

A planned program for rural growth should include the following:

1. Population redistribution. Government expenditures and policies should provide incentives for population redistribution in those areas where the natural resources and the social attitudes are such that population growth is desirable.

2. Improved services. Increased emphasis should be given to research and action programs that will bring rural services—particularly health, education and transportation—up to suburban standards.

3. Higher incomes. Efforts to increase levels of income for rural residents should be developed and accelerated. Given the means, rural people themselves will alleviate many of the inequities in services and amenities that currently exist between rural and urban areas.

4. Improved amenities. A research program to determine which amenities are most important to people in rural areas should be initiated. Action should be taken to protect and enhance these amenities as they are identified.

5. Construction of environmental prototype facilities. Prototype facilities and communities should be planned to enhance amenities and minimize environmental conflicts. Regional and community growth should be stimulated and prototype facilities should be built to test and demonstrate the feasibility of alternative schemes for growth in rural America.

EFFECT OF SOCIAL AND TECHNOLOGICAL CHANGE

The depopulation of rural America has been a long, steady process, but foreseeable social and technological changes may make it possible to stop and even reverse the trend. Over the next three decades, the following may be assumed:

1. Fewer people will be required to live in cities. As automation becomes increasingly widespread, less labor will be required for production industries. Increasingly sophisticated communication and transportation technologies will permit the decentralization of service industries. Greatly increased amounts of leisure time will encourage mobility. As a result, more and more people will be free to choose where they live, and the prime factors in their choice may not necessarily be economic.

2. Improved technology will make many services now associated with urban life available in rural areas. Two examples already reshaping the character of the rural American are television and mobile homes. Imagine the far-reaching effect that a low cost, lightweight, self-contained, energy-producing, water-cycling, waste-disposing, residential utility package would have on housing patterns. Such a core would make the "dwelling unit" independent of all fixed utility systems, and—combined with new transportation technologies—could offer a return, in a sense, to an almost nomadic life.

3. Many people will, if the above two conditions are satisfied, choose to live in rural surroundings. Economic necessity has been a prime factor in urban growth. In the future, physical or social amenities, or even the image of a desirable "life-style," may be dominant in choosing a place to live. Towns and villages offer a range of attractions that are not available at urban or suburban densities. Closeness to nature, quiet, clean air, open space, more intimate association with one's fellows, and a sense of community are unique aspects of town or village life. Small town or village life is not better nor worse than urban life; it is different, and the difference could lead to its survival and rebirth.

American culture has historically placed great emphasis on rural and small town life and the values associated with them. When this attitude is augmented by such characteristics of urban situations as pollution, noise, garbage strikes, and racial violence, it seems highly likely that many would choose to leave the city if they could. Indeed, a 1970 poll taken for *Life* magazine stated that ". . . of the 31% living in cities today, two-thirds would like to get out, and only a third wants to stay another 10 years" (Hooper, 1970).

Activities and programs of USDA substantially affect the settlement and use of rural America: (1) its extension–educational program; (2) its management of the national forests; and (3) the role of federal financial incentives on land use. Continuing USDA programs will be critical elements in efforts to shape rural growth and change.

Department of Agriculture programs for improving quality of rural life should be continuously evaluated in terms of the following essential principles:

Rural planning must be regional. A region is often best defined not so much by political boundaries as by topography, trade territory, climatic zones or socioeconomic conditions.

Regional diversity should be accepted and encouraged. This very diversity is an essential part of the amenity of rural America, and should be capitalized upon.

Planning must recognize the changing role of the farm in the rural landscape. The largest percentage loss in rural population over the last two decades has occurred in the farm population. While food and fiber production will continue a mainstay of the rural economy for decades to come, it is likely that other forms of activity will take on a much greater relative importance in that economy. Other land uses will become increasingly important in relation to traditional agriculture—land for roads, for example, and physical facilities for health, education and housing.

Rural redevelopment must be based on a network of interdependent communities. The day of the self-sufficient small town or village is gone, and nostalgia will not bring it back. Just as people now live in the surburbs and commute to the city to work, people may live in one location in the country, work in another, shop in a third, and spend their leisure time in yet another.

The size, location, density, and growth rate of new or revitalized communities should be planned to maximize the efficiency of education, medical and transportation service systems. While economy alone should not dictate population patterns, neither should haphazard private growth be allowed to overload the schools, overextend medical service systems, or clog transportation routes. The massive investment required to improve facilities must be selectively committed in order to encourage growth that optimizes service.

Planning must encourage the development and maintenance of a wide range of small communities of different types, densities, sizes, and physiographical characteristics. The countryside offers a social and physical setting very different from urban or suburban areas. To have a diverse array of viable settlements ranging in size from isolated farms to large city might well promote a more balanced and stable society. Such a diversity of choice could be considered a legitimate goal of government policy in itself, even at the cost of subsidizing settlements that, because of their size, are penalized by the free market (much as money is now spent to support certain cropping practices).

Settlements, transportation grids, and publicly used lands must be planned to preserve the integrity of the existing landscape. If immigration holds promise for rural renewal, it can also lead to rural destruction. The distinction between country and town is already blurred as commercial development in small communities moves out along the two-lane highway (just as the city moves out along its freeways). Nothing could be more troublesome than for a new wave of people to bury the unique character of the landscape under a blanket of undifferentiated rural suburbia. The USDA, through its educational–extension activities could do few things more valuable in protecting the character of our rural lands than to encourage the kind of rural zoning laws that would restrict roadside commercial-development penetration into farm and recreational lands.

DEVELOPMENT OF POVERTY AREAS

The cause of, and proposed remedies for, rural economic depression have been studied by others at length, notably by the President's National Advisory Committee on Rural Poverty. The problem is one for which there is no simple answer. A variety of causes require a variety of responses—ranging from large-scale re-education and relocation of people to providing incentives for location of job opportunities in rural areas. Rural poverty cannot be studied in isolation, but only as one aspect of a national policy for balanced urban–rural growth.

Government employment is a large factor in the national economy; investments in staffing and the location of facilities and programs—including those of USDA—can in themselves assist in alleviating depressed conditions. USDA should not only take such factors into consideration in making its own decisions but should consider selecting employees from poverty backgrounds for training and staffing.

RURAL AMENITIES

To encourage in-migration will require, in addition to providing an increased level of services, that the achievable amenities that would serve

as incentives for migration be identified (these amenities are not to be confused with those of the nostalgic small town image that, for the most part, no longer exists) and that programs be instituted to preserve, enhance, and create amenities capable of surviving in the face of a growing population influx.

The Committee recommends that the USDA institute a program of research to identify those attainable amenities most likely to motivate rural in-migration over the next 30 years. This program must not rely solely upon existing data or upon conditions, as they may reflect past and present social attitudes only. For example, existing user preferences for recreation—based on current facilities and the desires of a primarily urban population making infrequent excursions into the countryside—may be very different from those incentives that can convince people 15 years hence to make a permanent move. To discern the basic attitudes and motivation that could actually produce relocation will be difficult, requiring sophisticated research techniques; yet there are people in the United States today who typify many aspects of a future post-industrial population. These people are in good health, capable of a productive life, with mobility, leisure, and a permanent annual income high enough to give them flexibility in locational choice. Many people connected with such seasonal industries as timbering, farming, or fishing, for example, spend up to six months of the year in other parts of the country. Those people who retire from government service (particularly the armed forces) after 20 or 30 years of service, at the peak of their productive and earning capacity, are perhaps even more indicative of future trends.

As part of the overall research program, the Committee specifically recommends that an inventory of these people be made—an investigation including where they tend to locate and for what reasons. Such a survey should examine how much importance such people place on the traditional idea of fixed location, for many Americans—particularly among those retiring earlier than the traditional age, 65—have already developed near-mobile societies, i.e., the traveling trailer groups on the west coast, etc. This trend, thus far little considered in terms of future social or physical planning, could have far-reaching consequences for the future face of rural America.

Certain amenities can be identified now. Programs for their preservation and encouragement should be instituted immediately. One such program should be to improve the quality of rural waterways. The interrelation between agricultural practices and water quality is discussed elsewhere in this report, but municipal sewage discharge and industrial wastes—both of which would presumably increase under the kind of settlement we foresee—have further degrading effects. It is essential that the strictest measures be taken to control such discharge into rural waterways, particularly since the strenuous effort to attract industry to impoverished rural areas often engenders an unquestioning acceptance of the pollution such industry causes.

The economics of the agricultural market have produced a striking loss of diversity in the rural landscape. While monoculture is a logical response to the existing market, its effect on the future quality of the landscape should be studied, as should be the USDA programs that encourage it. Subsidies and financial incentives for the retention of hedgerows, stream vegetation, and woodlots should be studied as supplements or alternatives. Financial incentives for opening underused private lands to such restricted public use as hunting, fishing, hiking, or picnicking should also be considered.

Lastly, the effect of such large-scale and mostly unmodifiable incentives to population mobility as climate and regional topographic and ecological character should be studied, so that regions of high attractiveness can be selectively supported and so that regional differences—including those of landscape character—can be identified, protected and developed.

SERVICES IN RURAL AMERICA

The massive discrepancy between urban and rural services, particularly medical and educational, has been well-documented; it need not be elaborated here. After lack of employment opportunity, these service inadequacies have undoubtedly played the most significant role in depopulating rural America and, if unaltered—given our assumptions of social change—are likely to place rural areas at an even greater disadvantage in the future. The level of services offered must be sufficiently improved to lure a significant number of Americans out of metropolitan areas and back into the countryside; furthermore, the services themselves must be those that will attract a cross section of the American population, not just retired or jobless people. A broad range of facilities is, therefore, needed.

It is equally important to provide these services in a spatial distribution that will allow people to move back into the countryside without destroying the amenities they come to enjoy, without turning the countryside into a transcontinental low-density suburbia. The countryside should be different from city or suburb. The range of settlement and life-style options should not be narrowed. This means that services must be provided in a pattern that gives near-equal advantages to a wide range of settlement sizes, densities and locations—from growth centers of 25,000 people or more to small villages.

The more detailed discussion of transportation, medical, educational, and housing services is organized as follows:

- Description of a general research, planning, and evaluation program that would be common to the transportation, medical, and educational programs, tying them together in a single system. This commonality is important, for one of the major failures of past rural development is that these three service systems—insofar as they have been planned at all—have been planned separately and on a small scale, producing inconsistencies and conflicts in the three distribution patterns.
- Discussion of the special aspects of the transportation, medical, and educational systems, taken separately.
- A discussion of programs for improved rural housing, which is held separate for three reasons: Transportation, medical, and educational services form the basic regional service grid that will influence subsequent housing location; the transportation, medical and educational service systems depend almost entirely upon public financing and are almost completely subject to public planning; the first three systems require far more research on basic theory.

Rural Transportation, Medical and Education Services

Research and planning for the three service systems have different content and involve different disciplinary skills, but the basic processes are identical; the goal is a single integrated program.

This program must start with basic theoretical research. Most planning for these services has been done on an *ad hoc* basis, in response to pressures of the moment and short-range, fragmented goals and projections. Work aiming at larger social goals, that would tie the planning of these systems together into an integrated whole has simply not been done in the United States.

Much of the work must look to the future since the revitalization of rural America depends upon the shape of a future society distinctly different from that of today. The stages of the program are as follows:

Population projections. The optimal future rural population profile must be determined. Particular attention should be paid to regional differences.

Performance standards. The types and quality of health care to be made available to rural America should be determined in conjunction with the kinds and quality of education, and how quickly, easily, and at what cost, rural Americans will be able to take advantage of such services.

Future technological capabilities. Forecasting technological capabilities is a step that must be unrestrictedly forward-looking and imaginative in orientation. Future technologies—especially new communications- and information-handling techniques—could bring about a radical restructuring of health care and education systems; a radical increase in the level of health care available to rural dwellers is one potential outcome, for example.

Alternative regional delivery systems. Various models should be designed and tested for using future technologies to achieve the desired standards of care. Two points are essential: The models should not be designed on the basis of current conditions; and design should focus on the actual delivery of the services to the user, as distances and population densities of rural America have proved critical obstacles in current delivery systems. The design should pay particular attention to tradeoffs between permanent physical facilities, transportation (facility-to-user or user-to-facility) and telecommunication techniques. Alternative mixes of (1) specialized staffing and facilities, (2) more generalized facilities and staffing, and (3) paraprofessionals should also be investigated. The ultimate form of the model should include specifications relating to the geographical location and communications net of each system, including the staffing and funding required.

Comparison with existing conditions. Alternative proposed models that seem equally promising in the abstract might look very differently when evaluated in terms of the economic and social costs required in making a transition from what now exists. Also, a comprehensive national survey of those existing systems accepted by users from different regions and social backgrounds and those that are not—with the reasons for their use or nonuse—would be helpful in forecasting the success of proposed delivery systems.

Integration. The proposed transportation, medical and educational systems—each of which will have been developed with its own needs uppermost—must be compared with each other. Tradeoffs between the three systems will have to be made and one or more comprehensive systems models designed. These must then be compared with existing conditions and a final proposal accepted for an integrated, regional service system as a goal in rural planning.

The final product would be regional plans for the location and type of all medical and educational and transportation systems in rural

America to serve the population that will be attracted there over the next 20 or 30 years. This is a large but necessary goal.

Transportation   A thoughtfully planned transportation network, when coupled with a better communication network, is critical to providing other services in a pattern that maximizes their efficiency. It also has the potential to promote settlement patterns that are complementary and not destructive to the character of a rural landscape.

Existing transport technology, if available and comprehensively planned, is adequate to fill the future needs of rural America. The future network can be shaped by the private passenger automobile and such related systems as buses and minibuses. The automobile may threaten to choke our older cities, but, in the countryside, it offers a new freedom.

The basic planning unit of the new regional network might be called a "Domain of Convenience." It would be based upon driving times representing 20 minutes under average conditions along decent roads free from urban congestion (in area, a primary circle of perhaps 15-mile radius, or about 700 square miles). The basic goal of the new regional planning network would be to locate those facilities needed every day within such a radius. Some regions of the United States now have, and will continue to have, even in a revitalized countryside, a population density too low to support a small domain; here, the radius should be larger, but the principle remain the same. Some aspects of rural America are now being shaped in this way. School boards make locational decisions along such lines; many small town businesses survive or fail on this principle. A national planning commitment is needed, however, to plan settlements in this context.

Other complex, more expensive, or less often called-upon services should be located within somewhat larger domains. While access to elementary schools, for example, might be required in each domain, secondary education and higher education facilities could be located in larger units. Such a network would not necessarily require an elaborate road-building program or highly engineered construction solutions. Two departures from current planning standards would, however, be required.

First, the new network should depend largely upon the private automobile. (It would be interesting, perhaps, to compare potential savings in public transit against the money required to subsidize the purchase and operation of automobiles by rural families.) Bus service, an obvious supplement, need not take conventional forms, i.e., regularly scheduled movement of large vehicles. School buses might carry out other collecting functions rather than sitting idle much of the day. What might be called in-between solutions should not be overlooked: privately operated, part-time minibuses, or automobiles similar to taxicabs, or the now-departed jitney. The possibility of service-related transportation scheduling, such as regular pick-up of persons scheduled for preventive medicine, would be worth studying. The literature of urban transportation contains imaginative proposals for more efficient transport. Similar methods of analysis and design applied to rural transportation problems might turn up new and promising systems.

Second, principles of road location need to be completely studied and the system designed to deliver the educational, employment, and medical systems of the future most efficiently. Most facilities are now located to function within a road system designed years ago to respond to different needs and a different society. Conversely, roads are often planned or upgraded in response to pressures that may be short-lived, that often reflect special interests, and that are almost never planned to effect desired settlement patterns.

Basic research is needed in this area. Mathematical techniques such as network analysis and transportation-trips modeling, for example, should be an integral part of the planning process. Optimizing distribution within and between the proposed domains of convenience might well point toward a pattern far different from today's all-pervasive rectilinear grid, which very often ignores existing population concentrations, trip demand, and topography and was initially designed to serve the convenience of land survey and speculation, the farm as a dominant factor in rural life, and old patterns of farm-to-market travel.

An abstract, mathematically derived regional road system should not then be heedlessly translated into concrete and slapped across the face of rural America. If more than *ad hoc* changes in an obsolete system are to be achieved, however, a theoretical study of the most efficient future network is needed before any redesign actually begins. The cost of a postulated plan could then be compared with investment in existing facilities and the necessary adjustments made. The final design might require a pattern radically different than that of today, but it might well be that key changes in existing systems could bring about marked improvement without drastic changes in pattern. Until such a study is done, the answer to that question is not at hand.

Health Care   While the level of medical services available to some of the American people is rising, the urban–rural gap may well be widening. In a time of high medical technology, there are sectors of rural America where privies and midwives are still the rule. Through the mass media most rural people have become keenly aware of the kind of services available to some sectors of the population, if not to them. Planning for the future must be amenable and receptive to basic changes in the systems of medical and paramedical education, public health programs, and private and hospital practice.

Financing While the costs of the needed services will be high, the present direct and indirect costs of inadequate services are also high. For example, in sparsely settled and economically depressed areas of the country, such as the intermountain states, the need to travel 50 to 100 miles to secure medication, prenatal care, or routine physical examinations means that residents whose incomes are well below poverty levels are paying out large sums of money for what few services they manage to get. Furthermore, studies of the long-term costs to the state of providing welfare support to indigent citizens underscores the disproportionate amount that is going to maintain rural residents in substandard conditions.

A study should be made of the potential in rural areas for partial prepayment (possibly through a cooperative health insurance plan) for essential local health services and facilities. Some funds now being expended for inefficient care might be devoted to financing better systems; cooperative efforts to build needed facilities and underwrite new systems might be possible. The balance between privately and publicly financed programs should also be studied. Clearly, some approach other than the present public-services-for-the-destitute-or-unemployed versus private-services-for-the-employed is needed. Such a scheme leaves many lower- and middle-income families ill-served—especially in cases of catastrophic or chronic illness—and leads to duplication of services and facilities.

Staffing A major deficiency in rural health care lies in the difficulty of attracting people with the needed skills to rural areas, particularly in a time when the country as a whole faces a shortage of such personnel. One reason often given is isolation from professional colleagues and from special technical equipment and services. The massive rural delivery system here proposed would largely eliminate the scarcity of facilities and partially eliminate the isolation from colleagues and technical support, at least if the professionals were willing to accept electronic communications as a partial substitute for face-to-face contact. Another explanation for scarcity is that trained medical personnel do not practice in rural areas because the income there is not comparable to that in urban areas. But the fact remains that many potentially rewarding opportunities for medical practice are going begging all over rural America, and, if the monetary returns are perhaps not as great as in urban areas, neither are some of the attendant pressures. Even if the problem were simply one of low rural earning, it could be solved, if necessary, by offering a government subsidy to personnel locating in critical rural areas.

It is very likely that reasons other than economic ones are crucial, and it is essential that the question of motivation be thoroughly studied in terms of the entire structure of current medical practice and education. (L. Dilatush, B. Douglas, and G. Otis, School of Medicine, University of New Mexico, unpublished report, 1969.)

Current emphasis in medical training on the professional standards and financial advantages of highly specialized preparation, and on the treatment of complex illnesses rather than preventive measures or health maintenance, may well discourage interest in rural practice. The federal government should encourage the design and implementation of training programs aimed at preparing and motivating students for rural practice.

Many physicians and their wives, nurses, and other trained specialists typically come from backgrounds and from educational experiences that make them unlikely to desire the kind of social setting commonly associated with rural and small town life. Even those physicians who are motivated toward rural practice, and to whom the unhurried life and recreational advantages of smaller communities appeal, are inclined to have real reservations about their families—in particular, the kind of educational opportunities available in such communities. This circumstance makes clear the interrelatedness of the services and amenities needed to improve the attractiveness of rural America.

An overall program of revitalization would answer many of these reservations in time. However, other programs are needed immediately. Several possibilities exist: selecting medical students from a broader range of social and economic backgrounds than is presently the practice in most schools and providing support for their education; developing new professions and subprofessions for those who would be more likely to accept small town life; developing a system that ties training opportunities to required terms of service in small communities.

Education   The future rural education system must be diverse enough to attract a representative segment of the population. It must offer elementary school education of the caliber to attract families with high standards and maintain quality programs up through adult education of the kind that is in growing demand by retired people (such as "community college" offerings).

Advanced techniques of communication and information retrieval hold some promise for reversing trends toward urbanization and centralization. The massive consolidation of rural school districts over the last two decades was a response to the pressures of those times, but it hastened the decay or death of many small American communities. In many such places the school was the only meaningful link to mainstream America. The technology then available required bringing the student to the education; the technology of the 1970's and 1980's may enable us to take the education to the student.

New technology includes sophisticated audiovisual techniques and materials, closed-circuit television (including audio and eventually video feedback), and computer-based instruction. In addition to communications technology, new systems of staffing should be explored, such as the use of circuit-riding specialists and paraprofessionals. Imaginative use of new communications networks with the technology of a decade or two hence, and new staffing patterns, could bring a suitable education within reasonably convenient traveling distance of the most isolated parts of rural America. Not every small community would have a fixed year-round facility, but traveling teams of skilled people, supported by advanced technology, could visit even the smallest of communities for some periods during the year, ending the isolation they now endure. We do not envision an undifferentiated network of electronically automated one-room school houses, but a system that would give even the smallest of communities a contact with, and a stake in, the mainstream educational process of the country.

The benefit of such a system would lie not only in decentralization, but in flexibility to respond to changing population densities and profiles and to changing local needs. A system of compact, moveable electronic cores might be used for traveling service in specially remote areas. Other semipermanent or permanent cores could be plugged into structures less costly to build than today's highly equipped school houses, or located in renovated structures converted from other uses. Such flexibility would avoid a repetition of the 1950's and 1960's spectacle of expensive consolidated school plants standing under-used, and, in some cases empty, as populations shift.

Housing

According to the 1960 census, two thirds of the substandard housing in the United States was outside of the standard metropolitan statistical areas. More than a million rural homes were judged to be dilapidated. The rate of substandard occupied housing in rural areas was twice that of urban areas. Almost one third of rural families still used privies; less than 50 percent of rural homes at that time had central heating or piped water. The President's National Advisory Commission on Rural Poverty and the President's Task Force on Rural Development point out that housing is one of the major problems of rural America.

Part of this failure to act has stemmed from a bias towards urban problems; for, although housing assistance programs were not designed to improve urban housing at the expense of rural housing, they have in fact worked that way. The Federal Housing Authority has become a powerful factor in American housing, but the agency specifically designed to assist rural housing—the Farmer's Home Administration—has from the outset suffered from lack of funds and influence. For years, the role of both these agencies has been to guarantee private investment, not directly to build or finance. Predictably, a program thus based on private lending agencies was of more benefit to the urban areas where most of those institutions operate. The public housing programs in the 1950's and the 1960's aimed at a more direct intervention in housing supply, but they, too, concentrated on urban areas. Rural public housing is still scarce.

Programs of technical research have also tended to concentrate on urban situations—not only such federally sponsored progiams as HUD's Operation Breakthrough, but also university-based research on new structural and mechanical systems. Most such programs have focused upon high technology, particularly high density, high-rise housing. In essence, little building has taken place in rural America mostly because it is unprofitable.

There is no clear reason why rural housing must *per se* be more expensive than urban housing. Building costs fall into three categories: the cost of land and improvements, the cost of money, and the cost of construction. Obviously, the cost of land in rural areas—even allowing for the development of road and utilities—is not generally higher than in urban or suburban areas. There is no clear reason, either, why the cost of money should be higher in rural areas. Nor is there any clear reason why the cost of construction should be higher in rural areas; while diseconomies of scale and distance might raise the price of materials, and while certain skilled trades are more readily available in urban areas, these factors should be at least counterbalanced by the generally lower wage rates in rural areas.

A program to raise the quality of rural housing across the United States must focus on three things: a nationwide commitment to such a program and establishment of strong, direct, national, regional and state organizational structures to administer it; money to carry it out; and an action-oriented research program to develop a technology that can build millions of new and renovated units economically, quickly, and efficiently.

Extensive recommendations for restructured administrative and financial programs have been made by the President's National Advisory Commission on Rural Poverty. Among these recommendations are (1) centralization of authority for housing programs in both the executive and legislative branches of the federal government; (2) encouragement of local public housing authorities in all areas and counties containing significant amounts of substandard rural housing; (3) statewide nonprofit housing corporations; (4) allocation of a fixed percentage of all public housing funds for work in rural areas; (5) establishment of a nationwide federal home loan bank; (6) recognition of the fact that any loan-guarantee program for improving rural housing for the poor must by its nature entail "low-risk" loans; (7) expansion of the scope of funding programs to cover second-trust loans; (8) higher levels of permanent support for rent supplements in rural areas; (9) self-help construction and repair–renovation work; (10) action programs to eliminate discrimination in rural housing (the rural minority groups are the worst-housed segment); and (11) active use of federal muscle, including denial of funds if necessary, to encourage state and local implementation programs.

The major research needs are in the areas of (1) economical and easily built sewage and water systems, (2) techniques of utilizing the widespread low-level building skills available in rural America in meaningful self-help programs, (3) standardized mass-produced utility packages as cores for self-help shells or renovation of older structures, (4) acceptance of the mobile home as a housing unit, (5) development of planning standards that will minimize the tendency of mobile-home colonies to become slums, and (6) the use of mobile home or other prefabrication techniques for enclosing space. These tasks are not "basic research" in the usual sense. The technology required in most of these areas has already been designed or modeled in prototype. While fundamental research into baseline conditions of rural housing, the values associated with housing among various American subcultures, or the behavioral effects of the home environment on children are valuable for the future, the first priority is to get existing technologies off the drawing boards and in use. Obviously, because quality of housing has a high correlation with disposable income, any devices for increasing the income of the low-income segment of rural dwellers would be advantageous.

Through its support of State Experiment Stations and land-grant colleges, USDA has a strong orientation to and capability in research. Yet despite a recognition of the important factors affecting the quality of living, most USDA research, as evidenced by the areas of research delineated in its Rural Development Program, has been in very different subject areas and for a very different clientele.

In 1970 Clay L. Cochran, Chairman of the Board of Directors of the National Rural Housing Coalition (advocating a large-scale program of research into rural housing needs before the Senate Select Committee on Nutrition and Human Needs), said that research money " . . . should not be turned over to USDA's research service or to the land-grant colleges. We need action-oriented research, related to people, not rural sociology or agri-business minded research" (Cochran, 1971). It is easy to take offense at these statements and dismiss them. But it is worth-while to look at the traditional research orientation that provoked this reaction. In 1966, for example, the results of a study jointly sponsored by the USDA and the Association of State Universities and Land-Grant Colleges, listed ten major goals for agricultural research for decade 1967–1977. These goals were further broken down into 127 area goals. Of these 127, only one dealt with rural housing. Discussion of that goal, "Housing Needs of Rural Families," took up less than one page of text, two lines fewer than the discussion of research needed on "Bees and Other Pollinating Insects." The study projected a need for about 65-scientist-person-years devoted to rural housing research in the fiscal year of 1977, the end-point of the proposal program. This was less than half that proposed for "environmental stress in production of livestock and poultry" and one-sixth that proposed for research in the "culture and protection of ornamentals and turf." Thus, while traditional programs are still important, a reordering of priorities is necessary if the social ills of rural America are to be attacked.

Through its ties with major universities and its presence in rural America through the Extension Service, USDA could play a major role in research and action programs to make rural America a better place to live. But, before the Department undertakes programs in these fields, hard choices must be made. The task is one that requires full commitment. Small, nominal research programs will be unproduc-tive and—if they bring on jurisdictional jealousies—on balance, destruc-tive. Unless total federal funding is increased, to mount a meaningful effort may require diverting support from traditional work areas. The skills, training, and attitudes required in these problem areas will often be different from those in the scientific and extension areas long sup-ported by USDA. The clientele, and users, of these services may often have interests directly contradictory to those of other long-standing USDA clientele. If the Department is to become deeply involved in this work, it needs to define very precisely the problem areas to be assumed and their interrelationships with other problem areas and other governmental bodies.

RESOURCE
ALLOCATION

8

Land

Estimates of the land requirements for crops and domestic animals hinge on estimates of future food and fiber requirements for the nation. They also raise the question of how these requirements might be met in terms of the United States food and fiber production potential under varying assumptions. In approaching these issues, the Committee reviewed the study prepared for the National Water Commission (NWC) by the Center for Agricultural and Rural Development (CARD) at Iowa State University (Heady *et al.*, 1972), hereinafter referred to as the NWC Report. It is not only comprehensive but includes recent data in its analyses. The Committee, therefore, used it extensively in projecting food and fiber requirements, and potentials for meeting requirements, during the twentieth century.

The Committee also worked with CARD in calculating the consequence of removing certain fragile lands from agricultural production, i.e., to determine the effect of removing these lands upon costs and levels of production. This calculation exemplifies the kind of analyses that are needed to develop tradeoffs between environmental quality and the costs and amounts of food and fiber produced by agriculture.

Finally, the Committee reviewed assessments and projections developed by Resources for the Future, Inc., the National Advisory Commission on Food and Fiber, the Water Resources Council and the National Water Commission. Among these were: *Land for the Future* (Clawson *et al.*, 1960), *Natural Resources for U.S. Growth* (Landsberg, 1964), *Food and Fiber for the Future* (National Advisory Committee on Food and Fiber, 1967), and *The Nation's Water Resources* (U.S. Water Resources Council, 1968).

FOOD AND FIBER NEEDED

The NWC Report projects food and fiber requirements for the United States to the year 2000. Commodities included in the projection include corn, sorghum, wheat, barley, oats, soybeans, cotton, sugar beets, tame hay, wild hay, improved pasture, unimproved and woodland pasture, cropland pasture, public grazing lands, fruits, nuts, rice, vegetables, dairy products, pork, beef, broilers, turkeys, eggs, lamb and mutton and other livestock. These projections are derived on a per capita basis, using prices and levels of per capita income assumed to prevail in the year 2000. Per capita trends were projected from consumption trend data in light of price and income projections. These per capita consumption levels estimated for 1970, and projected to 2000, are shown in Table 12.

TABLE 12   Per Capita Consumption Levels in 1970 and Projected to 2000

Commodity	1970[a]	2000
Beef and veal (lb carcass wt.)	116.7	157.7
Pork (lb carcass wt.)	65	66.3
Broilers (lb ready-to-cook wt.)	39.1	40.7
Turkeys (lb ready-to-cook wt.)	8.3	8.6
Lamb and mutton (lb carcass wt.)	3.4	3.4
Dairy products (lb milk equivalent)	595	403.2
Eggs (number)	302	204
Corn (bushels)	1.26[b]	1.25
Barley (bushels)	0.84[b]	0.8
Wheat (bushels)	2.57[b]	2.58
Cotton (lb)	18.6[b]	12
Sugar beets (tons)	0.12[b]	0.11
Per capita disposable income (1970 dollars)	3420.00	5400.00[c]

SOURCE: NWC Report, Table 3.9, p. III-30.
[a] USDA, Economic Research Service, "National Food Situation," NFS-136 (May, 1971).
[b] 1969 per capita consumption levels: U.S. Department of Agriculture, Agricultural Marketing Service, "Food Consumption, Prices and Expenditures: Supplement for 1969," Washington, D.C. (Supplement to Agricultural Economic Report No. 138.) January, 1971.
[c] This is equivalent to the $4000 maximum used to calculate the commodity demands expressed in terms of 1970 prices.

In estimating food and fiber requirements for the year 2000, per capita consumption must be adjusted in terms of imports and exports. Accordingly, the NWC Report makes this adjustment by projecting the 1967–1969 average commercial and government exports and imports to the year 2000. Net exports of grains, oilmeals and cotton are reported in Table 13. Imports of beef and veal, lamb and mutton, pork and dairy products as shown in Table 14 are net imports as expressed on a per capita basis. Assumed exports of eggs, broilers and turkeys for the year 2000 are shown in Table 15. These exports are net exports after deducting imports.

TABLE 13   Grain, Oilmeal and Cotton
Net Export Projections for 2000

Commodity	Quantity Exported[a] (thousands)
Corn–sorghum	710,264 bushels
Oats–barley	51,292 bushels
Wheat	637,115 bushels
Oilmeals	218,992 cwt
Cotton lint	3,400 bales

SOURCE: NWC Report, Table 3.10, p. III-33.
[a] Average 1967–1969 commercial and government exports.

TABLE 14   Livestock and Livestock
Product Export and Import Projections
for 2000 Expressed as Net Imports

Commodity	Weight per Capita (lb)
Beef and veal (carcass wt.)	6.96
Lamb and mutton (carcass wt.)	0.67
Pork (carcass wt.)	1.09
Dairy products (milk equivalent)	6.44

SOURCE: NWC Report, Table 3.11, p. III-33.

TABLE 15   Egg, Broiler and Turkey Export and Import Projections for 2000 Expressed as Net Exports

Commodity	Total (millions)
Eggs	47 dozen
Broilers	167 lb[a]
Turkeys	42 lb[a]

SOURCE: NWC Report, Table 3.11, p. III-33.
[a] Ready to cook.

SUPPLY OF LAND

The NWC Report estimated the total land available for crops, pasture and hay in the year 2000 from the base of 1964, Table 16. In these projections, available land in 2000 is assumed to equal the maximum acreages harvested for each crop in recent years, including land in retirement programs. The acres in cropland and hay remain approximately steady. However, the total land in 2000 is slightly higher than in the base year 1964. Most of the increase comes from improved and cropland pasture. Some of this increase is a transfer from woodland and unimproved pasture because of pasture improvement measures. Although these estimates do not exclude future nonfarm uses, such uses do not

TABLE 16   Total Land Available in the United States for Crops Included in the NWC Report

	1964[a] (1,000 acres)	2000 (1,000 acres)
Cropland	264,018	264,111
Tame hay	57,067	58,007
Wild hay	10,347	10,347
Improved and cropland pasture	93,437	117,776
Woodland and unimproved pasture	533,230	526,418
Public grazing lands	291,384	291,384
TOTAL	1,249,483	1,268,043

SOURCE: NWC Report, Table 3.1, p. III-4.
[a] U.S. Department of Commerce, Bureau of the Census, *U.S. Census of Agriculture, 1964.* Volume 1, Statistics for the States and Counties. Washington, D.C., 1967.

U.S. Department of Agriculture, "Crop Production, 1965 Annual Summary: Acreage, Yield and Production by States," Washington, D.C., CRPR 2-1 (65), December 20, 1965.

TABLE 17 Land Available for Irrigation in the 17 Western States for Crops Included in the NWC Report

	1964[a] (1,000 acres)	2000 (1,000 acres)
Cropland	14,129	18,557
Tame hay	6,734	7,442
Wild hay	1,355	1,355
Improved and cropland pasture	5,093	5,093
Other[b]	4,572	5,092
TOTAL	31,883	37,539

SOURCE: NWC Report, Table 3.2, p. III-4.

[a] U.S. Department of Commerce, Bureau of the Census, *U.S. Census of Agriculture, 1964.* Volume 1, Statistics for the States and Counties. Washington, D.C., 1967.

[b] Includes fruits, nuts, vegetables, rice and field seed crops for which water is allocated in 2000.

appear sufficient to affect available land appreciably, particularly because additional land could come into use from retirement and other uses.

An increase of 81 million people would take at most 20 million acres for urban uses (Krause, 1971). Krause estimates that about half this would come from a 2 percent decrease in current cropland. Much of this cropland, however, is already in transition toward urban uses and presently is contributing little to agricultural production. If future needs demand, an additional 49 million acres—besides a similar amount currently held in land retirement programs—could be brought into production (USDA, 1971c). This land, primarily from the major field crops, comes from the 243 million acres in land classes I-III that are now in forests, pasture and range. Thus, ample land could apparently be brought into farm uses to offset land needed for nonfarm uses. The key issue arises in planning an orderly transition to the nonfarm uses.

Land available for irrigation in the 17 western states in 1964 and projected to 2000 is shown in Table 17. The projected data for 2000 include new irrigated lands in Bureau of Reclamation projects that possess development potential by 1980.

MEETING THE REQUIREMENTS

In assessing national demands for food and fiber in relation to the land supply in 2000, additional variables must be considered. These variables, as specified in the NWC Report, include population growth, technological advance, nature of farm policies and cost of water. These variables are in addition to income, preferences and exports (including imports), which were discussed earlier.

Models A and B of the NWC Report were used here. Model A[1] assumes (1) free markets, (2) a population of 300 million by the year 2000, (3) current water prices,[2] (4) agricultural exports projected at the 1967–1969 level in 2000, and (5) production technologies projected from the trend of the period 1920–1970. Model B differs from Model A only in that the population estimate is 280 million people in 2000.[3]

Models A and B produce the estimates of livestock and livestock products for 2000 shown in Table 18. Actual production for the year 1969 is also shown. Estimated livestock in 2000 under Model A would require the feed shown in Table 19. Feed for livestock, plus other needs for major food crops, would require the annual production in 2000 that is summarized in Table 20. Using the yields as summarized in Table 21 for conditions specified for Models A and B, the acreages needed in 2000 are shown in Table 22. Dryland and irrigated crops are shown separately because of the marked extremes in yields. The projected distribution of the production of annual crops, hay and pasture and selected livestock by Model A in 2000 is shown for the major river basins (Figure 5) in Tables 23 and 24.

Land and water are adequate for meeting projected United States food and fiber requirements for the year 2000 under both Models B (280 million people) and A (300 million people). However, these projections for 2000 are based on assumptions of land use in a maximum benefit situation, with a moderate increase in production per unit and a level of exports equal to that of 1967–1969. Deviations from these assumptions can be influenced by government policies. Projections such as those of the NWC Report should be updated periodically as supply and demand for food change and as changes occur in government policy.

---

[1] The NWC Report carries results of three variations of Model A in terms of Models A1, A2, and A3, which increase water prices to $15.00, $22.50 and $30.00 per acre foot, respectively. Also, the report carries results of Models C and D. Model C introduces a land retirement program, and Model D uses the 325 million population projection for the year 2000 and a more advanced level of technology. Neither Models C and D nor the variations of Model A are referenced further in this report of the Committee.

[2] Present water prices per acre foot vary from $0.85 in water supply region 25 to $57.96 in water supply region 16. See Table 3.6, p. III-18 of the NWC Report.

[3] This 280 million population projection for the year 2000 is the "D" level projection by the United States Department of Commerce. The "C" and "B" levels are 300 and 325 million, respectively.

TABLE 18 Livestock and Livestock Product Manufacture in the United States as Projected under Models A and B for 2000

Item	Unit	Actual 1969[a]	Projected Model A	Model B
Dairy cows	thousand head	14,106	8,573	8,020
Beef cows	thousand head	36,002	85,395	79,768
Beef feeding	thousand head	24,022	63,705	59,464
Hogs	thousand head[b]	84,958	138,978	135,619
Milk	million cwt	1,120	1,187	1,108
Lamb and mutton	thousand cwt[c]	5,082	8,478	7,262
Broilers	thousand cwt[c]	80,540	123,472	115,354
Turkeys	thousand cwt[c]	16,140	26,220	24,440
Eggs	million dozen	5,757	5,206	4,685

SOURCE: NWC Report, Table 4.51, p. IV-122.

[a] U.S. Department of Agriculture, Dairy Situations DS-335, Washington, D.C., May 1971.

U.S. Department of Agriculture, Livestock and Meat Situations LMS-122, Washington, D.C., March 1970.

U.S. Department of Agriculture, Poultry and Egg Situations PES-266, Washington, D.C., June 1970.

U.S. Department of Agriculture, Statistical Reporting Service, Cattle on Feed, Cattle Sold for Slaughter: Selected Markets, January 1, 1970 Mt. An. 2-1 (1-70), Washington, D.C., January 16, 1970.

[b] All values for hogs in 2000 calculated by dividing total production by 220 pounds to get number of head.

[c] Lamb and mutton reported in carcass weight and broilers and turkeys reported in ready-to-cook weight.

TABLE 19 Feed Consumption by Livestock in the United States under Model A Projections for 2000

Class	Feed Grains (1,000 bushels)	Oilmeals[a] (1,000 cwt)	Wheat (1,000 bushels)	Forages[b] (1,000 tons)
Beef cows	270,963	457	0	539,690
Beef feeding	2,202,177	117,937	500,133	66,626
Dairy	743,391	93,056	12,185	46,178
Hogs	1,814,267	174,457	335,264	0
Sheep and lambs	15,163	8,575	73	8,483
Broilers	367,160	151,776	1,727	0
Turkeys	140,917	65,573	7,080	296
Eggs	314,404	64,348	19,194	531
Other	400,039	7,680	0	0
TOTAL	6,268,481	683,859	875,656	661,804

SOURCE: NWC Report, Table I-1, p. I-1.

[a] Includes soybean and cottonseed oilmeals.

[b] Includes tame hay, wild hay, corn and sorghum silage, and all pasture in hay equivalent tons.

TABLE 20   Total Productions of Annual Crops under
Model A Projections for 2000

Crop	Production (thousands)
Wheat (bushels)	2,286,022
Corn grain and grain sorghums . (bushels corn equivalent)	5,953,594
Barley and oats (bushels barley equivalent)	1,689,367
Corn and sorghum silage (wet tons)	269,698
Soybean and cottonseed oilmeals (cwt soybean oilmeal equivalent)	843,839
Hay and pasture (tons hay equivalent)	578,183

SOURCE: NWC Report, Table H-2, p. H-2.

TABLE 21   Yields of Annual Crops, Hay and Pasture in the United States as Projected under Models A and B for 2000

		Model A		Model B	
Crop	Unit	Dryland Yield	Irrigated Yield	Dryland Yield	Irrigated Yield
Corn grain	bushel/acre	112.0	121.0	115.9	124.6
Corn silage	ton/acre	19.1	32.9	21.4	32.9
Grain sorghum	bushel/acre	77.5	128.3	81.0	128.0
Sorghum silage	ton/acre	15.6	28.4	15.8	28.4
Wheat	bushel/acre	40.0	107.6	40.6	110.7
Oats	bushel/acre	65.4	77.7	65.1	82.9
Barley	bushel/acre	60.0	85.7	56.9	80.0
Soybeans	bushel/acre	37.6	30.6	37.4	0
Sugar beets	ton/acre	27.2	48.1	27.2	0
Cotton	bale/acre	2.2	4.2	2.1	4.5
Tame hay	ton/acre	2.5	5.1	2.9	5.3
Wild hay	ton/acre	1.1	1.7	1.0	1.7
Improved and cropland pasture[a]	ton/acre	1.4	2.6	1.4	2.6
Other pasture[a]	ton/acre	0.1	0	0.1	0

SOURCE: NWC Report, Table H-1, p. H-1.
[a] Hay equivalent. Other pasture includes unimproved permanent pasture, woodland pasture and public grazing lands.

TABLE 22 Acreages Required for Annual Crop, Hay and Pasture Yields Projected under Models A and B for 2000

Crops	Dryland Acres in 18 River Basins (1,000 acres)	Irrigated Acres in 9 Western River Basins (1,000 acres)
Wheat	53,137	1,496
Corn grain	53,572	909
Grain sorghum	24,076	2,534
Oats	20,543	411
Barley	7,009	338
Soybeans	45,780	8
Cotton	4,297	383
Sugar beets	1,076	70
Silage	13,712	1,070
Tame hay	85,409	9,805
Wild hay	8,902	1,249
Pasture	929,599	4,301
Fruits, nuts, rice and vegetables	–	4,697

SOURCE: NWC Report, Tables 4.2 (p. IV-7), 4.3 (p. IV-13), 4.4 (p. IV-17), and 4.5 (p. IV-20).

FIGURE 5 Location of river basins as delineated by the Water Resources Council.

TABLE 23 Production of Annual Crops in the 18 River Basins under Model A Projections for 2000

River Basin	Wheat (1,000 bushels)	Corn Grain and Grain Sorghum[a] (1,000 bushels)	Barley and Oats[b] (1,000 bushels)	Corn and Sorghum Silage[c] (1,000 tons)	Soybean and Cottonseed Oilmeals[d] (1,000 cwt)
New England	0	0	4,556	0	0
Middle Atlantic	140,164	0	133,949	0	5,165
South Atlantic-Gulf	31,287	76,480	140,588	12,433	123,095
Great Lakes	65,562	409,313	154,204	13,943	65,337
Ohio	124,253	1,076,113	69,784	7,920	120,436
Tennessee	0	0	0	0	10,199
Upper Mississippi	225,049	2,292,743	188,391	79,020	234,825
Lower Mississippi	266,445	0	0	0	126,121
Souris-Red-Rainy	58,898	64,655	453,145	12,509	0
Missouri	527,500	796,801	364,967	62,647	138,458
Arkansas-White-Red	321,252	402,391	28,613	49,530	15,621
Texas-Gulf	84,532	615,328	26,851	6,719	288
Rio Grande	0	74,189	1,756	3,923	414
Upper Colorado	0	3,130	921	823	0
Lower Colorado	0	0	27,182	0	0
Great Basin	6,269	0	10,499	9,289	0
Columbia-North Pacific	389,333	14,445	36,333	7,247	0
California-South Pacific	45,478	128,006	47,628	3,695	3,880
TOTAL (United States)	2,286,022	5,953,594	1,689,367	269,698	843,839

SOURCE: NWC Report, From Table H-2, p. H-2.
a Corn equivalent.
b Barley equivalent.
c Wet tons.
d Soybean oilmeal equivalent.

124

TABLE 24 Production of Hay and Pasture and Selected Livestock in the 18 River Basins under Model A Projections for 2000

River Basin	All Hay and Pasture[a] (1,000 tons)	Dairy Cows (1,000 head)	Beef Cows (1,000 head)	Beef Feeding (1,000 head)	Hogs[b] (1,000 head)
New England	591	0	0	0	0
Middle Atlantic	5,370	1,619	435	497	3,737
South Atlantic–Gulf	27,499	3,967	517	612	177
Great Lakes	32,818	887	5,511	448	42,272
Ohio	5,696	0	5,653	0	0
Tennessee	64,687	0	4,318	0	58,310
Upper Mississippi	16,366	0	3,051	0	0
Lower Mississippi	8,638	0	11,485	0	0
Souris–Red–Rainy	161,039	0	24,718	5,990	40,797
Missouri	83,966	0	14,221	22,261	0
Arkansas–White–Red	44,946	328	0	22,499	0
Texas–Gulf	16,759	557	6,192	4,144	0
Rio Grande	8,237	0	2,527	1,946	0
Upper Colorado	5,737	1,150	0	437	0
Lower Colorado	8,601	0	0	0	0
Great Basin	27,905	0	2,453	1,824	0
Columbia–North Pacific	28,175	61	4,016	3,041	0
California–South Pacific					
TOTAL (United States)	578,183	8,569	85,387	63,699	145,293

SOURCE: NWC Report, Table H-3, p. H-3.

[a] Hay equivalent.

[b] Hog production assumes a live weight of 220 pounds.

125

WORLD FOOD DEMAND

Although the world demand upon American acres for food is not the central concern of this report, it merits brief attention. World needs are directly related to the world population, which now exceeds 3.4 billion, is increasing at least 2.2 percent per annum, and by the year 2000 is predicted to approach 7 billion (Hauser, 1964). In Asia, South America and Europe this population is expected to strain food production, especially protein-production capabilities.

The established per capita minimal protein requirements for man is 60 g/day, as 7 grams from animal, 17 grams from pulse (legume seed), and 36 grams from vegetable and cereal proteins (Pawley, 1963; Brown, 1963). These minimal standards as applied to the estimated population totals lead to estimated human protein requirements as shown in Table 25.

The domestic livestock protein demands are about 315×10^6 metric tons/year. At least 75 percent of this demand (or 222×10^6 metric tons) is noncompetitive with man. The 1:4 ratio of human minimal protein requirement to livestock minimal requirement leads to the estimated human plus livestock protein demand of 375, 540 and 800 million metric tons/year in 1960, 1980 and 2000, respectively (White-Stevens, 1967).

The annual production of protein during 1960-1970 is shown in Table 26. The minimal protein demand during this period was approximately 75×10^6 metric tons/year. The third World Food Survey of FAO (UN-FAO, 1963) showed that serious nutritional gaps occurred recently

TABLE 25 Estimated Minimum World Human Protein Demands Based on Projected Population Increases for 1980 and 2000

Source	Annual Demand (metric tons × 10^6)		
	1960	1980	2000
Animal	11	15	23
Pulse	16	23	34
Cereal	48	70	103
TOTAL	75	108	160

SOURCE: (White-Stevens, 1967).

TABLE 26   Estimated Annual World
Production of Proteins for Human Consumption for the Period 1960–1970

Source	Annual Protein Production (metric tons X 10^6)
Cereals	65
Oilseeds	16
Pulses	5
Roots and tubers	5
Animal–meat, eggs, milk	19
Fish	8
TOTAL	118

SOURCE: UN–FAO Yearbooks, vols. 20–24
(1966–1970).

in South America (5%), Africa (6%), West Asia (3%), free Far East (60%), and Communist Far East (25%).

The world need for food, especially protein, suggests that the American food exports can substantially affect the demand for food production in the United States. The magnitude of this demand will depend on many factors: United States policies to encourage agricultural exports, the ability of United States farmers to produce food competitively on the world market, the ability of foreign countries to buy and distribute United States food, the rate of increase in food production in those countries that are markets for United States food, and foreign policies concerning importation of food.

Not all food and fiber producing industries would be affected to the same magnitude by export. For example, the United States soybean market is sensitive to international demands because of the relatively large quantity of soybeans that is normally exported.

Continued expansion of United States exports faces considerable competition. The European Common Market (ECM), the largest competitor, has increased grain production 40 percent within the last decade, with a consequent decline of grain imports from 13.3 to 2.5 X 10^6 metric tons (Palmby, 1971). This declining demand, however, appears to be ephemeral because of the vagaries of northern European weather, the rising standard of living and increased meat consumption (UN–FAO, 1969), particularly of cereal consuming livestock (Borsody, 1966). Thus, in 1970–1971 the ECM again imported 10 X 10^6 metric tons of grains (Palmby, 1971). Japan, formerly a grain deficient country, has also

applied western technology to her restricted farmlands and produced a
surplus of rice (UN–FAO, 1968).

The potential impact of world demands on United States food production is large indeed. This demand is, however, contingent upon so
many factors that precise prediction is virtually impossible.

LAND-USE POLICY

Agricultural land-use policy is of increasing importance as the scale
of coordinated land and resource planning extends from metropolitan
areas to states and regions. But such policy and planning is a fundamental and inseparable part of a national and international complex
and must be developed in this larger context. In the light of these considerations, certain approaches are recommended:

- Continued examination, on a national scale, of the consequences
of proposed changes. This is illustrated by the example summarized
in the Appendix.
- Development of rural areas for population redistribution wherever
the carrying capacity of land and resources permits; urban redevelopment and intensification, on a selective basis where support systems
are adequate.
- Redevelopment of depressed, poverty stricken, or environmental
disaster areas in the country.
- Conversion of some agricultural land into better and more diverse
patterns as regards environmental conflicts, access to markets, and
preservation of fragile lands.
- Protection of first-class farmland where urbanization is rampant,
assuring enough productive land to provide sufficient food and fiber for
at least 20–30 years and for crops requiring specific climate or soils.
- Accumulation of survey data on topography, soil, agriculture, waterways, climate, population and culture need to effectuate national
policies.

The American public has been slow to accept the concept of regional planning. This is often explained as a reflection of the "pioneer
spirit" and its freewheeling, energetic, competitive role in developing
the country. This spirit carried with it a strong resistance to land-use
controls of any kind. As a result, zoning as an implementation tool
still exists mainly at a local level and, even then, its effectiveness is
uncertain. Effective and comprehensive county, state and regional
planning is rare, as are zoning laws at these larger scales.

Despite the fact that federal funding of more diverse housing and public works projects is predicated on the prior adoption of a comprehensive plan, such plans seldom have power of enforcement beyond the local level. In most cases, special interest groups seem able to get almost anything they want through appeal boards or other avenues.

Matters may improve as the scale enlarges. State and regional planning may have a somewhat better chance of success because the number of "clients" is much greater, and this poly-client or institutional mosaic promises to be less vulnerable to special-privilege distortions of the sort that have afflicted local areas. In addition, there is increasing public awareness of the importance of planning as a requisite of environmental protection.

A MECHANISM FOR IMPLEMENTING A NATIONAL LAND-USE POLICY

Land-use policy, planning and implementation are the responsibility of agencies other than USDA. A significant part of the federally-owned land is managed through the Department of the Interior. A number of other federal agencies are concerned with both privately-owned and federally-owned land. It is unlikely, then, that land-use planning will be coordinated and effective unless there is a major reorganization of federal responsibilities in this area. The following mechanism is suggested as one means of achieving coordination:

1. Creation of a new board or council on National Growth and Land-Use Policy in the Office of the President. The Council on Environmental Quality, the Urban Growth Council of the Domestic Council and the Water Resources Council are recognized to be of national importance and thus are a part of the executive branch of the government. The proposed National Growth and Land-Use Policy Council could combine the functions of these councils under one comprehensive unit responsible for developing policy and guidelines for national growth and land use and for stimulating the development of state and regional land-use plans.

2. Formation of new legislative committees on National Growth and Land-Use Policy in both houses of Congress. Issues of national growth, change and land-use policy are now to be found in several congressional committees, such as the committees on Interior and Insular Affairs. Jurisdiction over comprehensive land-use and growth problems is therefore not clear-cut.

3. Establishment of a national data-bank inventory and monitoring

system for land characteristics on a major scale. Data banks of information on topography, soil capability characteristics, drainage, rainfall, waterways, fragile environmental areas, agricultural, mineral and energy resources, population distribution, service corridors, and cultural artifacts are now widely scattered in various government bureaus, universities, and private firms. Comprehensive planning on a regional and national scale is therefore severely limited by inadequacies and inconsistencies of information.

4. Implementation of funding and incentive programs to aid states and regional planning agencies. Existing and proposed legislation falls far short of the funding necessary to carry out comprehensive planning beyond a local level; incentives are particularly weak in assuring interstate coordination and consistency in the larger domains of regional planning. Massive aid in implementing state and regional plans should be contingent on the quality of the plans developed and their conformity with guidelines on national growth and land-use policy. Several recommendations made elsewhere in this report, such as those relating to formation of Environmental Process teams, Environmental Awareness centers, and Rural Development Service systems, would be components of such an implementation procedure.

Cropland has traditionally been considered consumable—a land bank for urban and industrial development. The fact that good cropland is usually flat and well-drained makes it the path of least resistance for urban growth, even though such urban expansion could be directed along the more linear patterns formed by the marginal lands that are usually present around urban areas. Since land development in much of America—particularly in the prairies and other relatively flat landscapes—was based on a grid system, farm property lines and farming patterns have tended to follow the grid. This same grid is also the convenient structure for industrial and residential expansion even when it results in loss of croplands. Such expansion not only reduces the food production capacity of suburban land but also imposes a monotonous grid on urban growth that conceals, rather than reinforces and enriches, the diversity of human settlement.

EFFECT OF ENVIRONMENTAL POLICIES

Environmental and agricultural predictions of acreage needs and demand must take into account the consequences of imposing constraints on things that are now unconstrained. For example, one could examine how much prices and crop acreage would change if pesticides were prohibited or if fertilizer use were restricted. The results of these constraints can be predicted without actually imposing the constraints; hence, common sense requires that these analyses be carefully made before such restrictions are enacted.

Simulation techniques may be used to predict the effects of environmental constraints if the coefficients and assumptions are valid. Because of the uncertainty of any set of coefficients to accurately predict future trends, the example in the Appendix does not imply endorsement of the specific coefficients used. In this case, the results of removing fragile land seem clear. Several crops would rise in price about 10 percent. Cattle and hogs would also cost about 10 percent more, while milk would increase only about 3 percent.

These data raise the question of how much more in food prices consumers are willing to pay to improve the quality of their environment. In making this decision, there will be tradeoffs between the two objectives—environmental quality and food prices. The tradeoffs will continue until people reach the point of indifference between a little more environmental quality and a little less food availability at a slightly greater cost. With knowledge of the tradeoffs, this optimum point can be predicted. Simulations can also help dispel illusions of sinister forces destroying our environment or raising the cost of food.

9

Recreation
and
Rural Growth

The demand for land and water for recreation is increasing (U.S. Department of the Interior, 1967). This increased demand can be met through multiple use of agricultural and forest land or by removing land from production and dedicating it exclusively to recreation. Thus, the impact of recreation upon food and fiber production is significant (McCormack, 1971).

TRENDS IN OUTDOOR RECREATION ACTIVITY

Prediction of needs for outdoor recreation facilities is difficult (Cicchetti, 1971). The uncertainty is intensified by the fact that the demands themselves are highly diverse. Daily recreation (tennis, swimming), weekend recreation (state parks), and wilderness recreation involve very different travel time and costs. Other complicating elements are social, psychological, financial and geographic factors that, if removed, would drastically change recreational demand (Clawson, 1959). Certain other questions must be answered before accurate predictions can be made:

- How much will leisure time change?
- Is there a latent demand for recreation opportunity?
- What will be the trend in level of disposable income?
- How much are people willing to pay?

- What type of facilities do they want?
- What portion of the recreation facilities should be resource-based?
- What parts will public agencies and private enterprise each play?

Even so, a few general trends can be predicted (Clawson, 1959; NAS, 1969a). The Bureau of Outdoor Recreation, recognizing that Americans continue to turn to the outdoors for recreation, has predicted that by the year 2000, summertime outdoor recreation will be 4-times greater than in 1960 (U.S. Department of the Interior, 1967). In 1960, there were nearly 4.3 billion individual "occasions" of outdoor recreation activity, and, by 2000, 16.9 billion are expected.

Between 1960 and 1965, Americans increased their use of outdoor recreation facilities 51 percent. By 1980, participation in the 19 major summertime outdoor recreation activities is expected to increase by at least 56 percent over the 1965 base. This trend is expected to continue, but at a somewhat slower rate of increase, to the year 2000 (U.S. Department of the Interior, 1967). The very activities showing the greatest amount of change also require the greatest amount of open space, water areas, and recreation facilities.

LAND FOR RECREATION FROM AGRICULTURE

The land of the United States totals about 2.3 billion acres. The "lion's share" of the total area (59%) is privately owned. Federal ownership is slightly more than a third, and state and local governments hold 5 percent (USDA, 1971a). About half is used for crops and livestock, with an additional 22 percent in ungrazed forest land. Only 5 percent of the land is in parks, recreation areas, wildlife refuges, etc.

Two million acres of land each year are converted from agricultural to nonagricultural uses (USDA, 1971c). The amount of cropland is decreasing at an annual rate of 3 percent. Irrigated farmland is increasing at the rate of 2 percent per year. Forest land is decreasing. Special use areas—including urban areas, highways and roads, military reservations, and farmsteads—have been on the increase as have been recreational areas such as parks and wildlife areas (USDA, 1971c).

Not only the amount, but the kind, of land demanded for recreation is important. Location relative to concentrations of people is certainly a key feature. An increasingly mobile citizenry, of course, has not only a regional recreation destination pattern up to 100 miles or more, but also a pattern of much further distances in certain seasons. This mobility lessens the pressure upon cropland near cities by making less fragile land nearby accessible for such uses as parks and golf courses.

Patterns of recreation are influenced by historic sites associated with cultural development and by camping and other sports associated with land and water. These patterns tend to follow river, mountain or coastal features, along which the vast majority of scenic, cultural and sports-related activities accumulate. All this tends to decrease competition between crops and recreation. Although future recreation will undoubtedly follow this same general pattern, the increasing use of off-road vehicles may drastically alter this historic tendency. The trail bike and snowmobile, for example, already threaten fragile wilderness areas as well as developed land. Here competition between recreation and crops or forest becomes intense.

A more optimistic note comes from another aspect. Most futurists predict sharp increases in educational forms of recreation, such as wildlife study, and forms of environmental education that require physical mobility and space. The likely effect of this shift would be to make recreation a much more diverse human activity, more difficult to distinguish from living and working space as an explicit land use and less competitive with agriculture than, say, the snowmobile.

The general conclusion is that for a long time there will be land adequate for agriculture and recreation. To extend that period, certain measures can be suggested:

• The Committee recommends that land-use policy combine recreation programs with land and water conservation programs, so that they act in concert in the competition with urbanization.

• Since much of the pressure for additional outdoor recreation opportunities will be directed toward agricultural, forest and fragile lands, the impact of recreational demand on food and fiber production should be continually examined (Kneese, 1970; Goldstein, 1971; National Science Foundation, 1971).

• The extent and locations where recreation will conflict with agricultural production and vice versa should be determined accurately.

• The competition between agriculture and recreation should be lessened by encouraging the development of the recreation potential of agricultural land, thus increasing both recreation and production, especially the recreational potential of national forests.

RURAL GROWTH

At the present time urban development is annually taking about 3 times as much land as transportation does and half as much as recreation.

Nevertheless, these losses from agriculture can be sustained for a while. How, then, can competition between agriculture and living space be lessened? And how can the living be made more pleasant?

Certain things are obvious. Cropland is saved and life made more pleasant if a house is built at the edge of a ravine rather than in the middle of a cornfield. It is reasonable to ask that governments encourage such common sense.

To plan growth, development and land use in a manner that will enhance the quality of the landscape and minimize environmental conflicts requires a team approach, as exemplified by the Environmental Awareness Center at the University of Wisconsin. Here, groups of specialists are organized into an environmental process team. In developing a regional plan, they first seek to determine the local environmental need—that is, the physiological and psychological requirement—then to integrate the environmental needs with the natural resources of the region. Initially, the desirable growth criteria for settlement are identified by a natural and earth sciences team, which determines the carrying capacity of the land, and by the human and health sciences team, which determines the physical and sociological needs of man. Next, remote sensing techniques are used to determine the topography of the natural resources on a regional basis, and architects have their input through the "form-giver" team. Finally, an implementation team takes the information from the form givers and puts it together in a simulation laboratory—alternatives are thereby derived and demonstration centers for environmental concepts may be built.

Prototypes seem to hold some promise as means to test whether rural development can be stimulated and agriculture simultaneously safeguarded. The Economic Development Agency (EDA) has established its "growth center" concept, which selects certain cities (usually small) and regions in the country for priority in developing employment opportunities and other economic attractions. These growth centers range across the United States in a regional pattern closely conforming to reports of depopulation in economically poor areas of the country. They are mostly in the South Central and Southern regions. Where these areas coincide with reasonably viable economic growth criteria and environmental impact criteria, they are designated for coordinated planning and expansion.

The Committee recommends that the principle of demonstration sites or environmental prototypes be strongly affirmed. The success of demonstration models will be greater if site-selection criteria as suggested below are carefully applied:

Ideally, a demonstration site should provide the widest feasible diversity (of age, income, ethnic and life-style groups, of physical and ecological characteristics) and be physically large enough in population and land area to be capable of widespread application elsewhere.

It should be clearly defined. A consistent regional identity becomes clearest at its edges, whether the edge definition is sharp (a water edge, for example) or in the nature of a transition zone to another region. (This concept of defined edge does not refer to political boundaries—although in some cases they may coincide.) Examples of regions defined in this way are Appalachia; Upper Peninsula, Michigan; San Diego County, California; Southampton, Long Island; Willamette Valley, Oregon; Mogollon Rim, Arizona and New Mexico.

Some of the demonstration sites should contain prime agricultural land in the paths of urbanization. Almost a half million acres of land are consumed annually by urban sprawl; a large portion of this acreage is agricultural land of high productivity, particularly in the Midwest. This land, and nonagricultural land now providing open space and green belts around urban areas, has virtually no effective protection. Although some zoning constraints and land management schemes attempt to control the growth urban edge, there is as yet no consistent national or regional growth policy in operation.

The demonstration sites should reflect rural problems and be able to absorb more people. In line with current USDA rural development policy and EDA growth center policy, rural poverty areas should have a high priority in assignment of federal funds through new and existing programs. Some such poor areas should be selected as demonstration sites and high priority be given in the employment and housing component of comprehensive planning for them.

The sites should differ in natural amenities. Attractive features, such as a mild climate, beauty of setting and uncrowded settlement, are to be found in many parts of the country that could accept considerable additional growth without damage. These very features have caused massive migration to the Southwest—in many cases beyond the supply of water, power, pollution control and transport. It is therefore necessary to demonstrate better density and wiser population distribution in areas that already attract people.

It should be possible through more radical environmental changes to develop amenities in areas of the country that are not greatly blessed by nature, but have capacity to support considerable growth. One such example is the use of a dome as proposed for the Minnesota Experimental City. This ambitious joint effort by the University of Minnesota, Minnesota business, and governmental institutions, supported by large federal grants, began in 1967. It will program, design and build a new city of 250,000 as a model for colder areas. Buckminster Fuller has suggested a partial application of the geodesic dome enclosure system to achieve the climate control and other advantages of a year-round "greenhouse."

The Environmental Design subcommittee of the Committee on Agriculture and the Environment has suggested that the prototype might best be developed by entrusting the work of defining rural development problems, selecting demonstration sites, planning, building, testing and evaluating results to a single "client" or authority, to maximize efficiency and quality of performance. There is already considerable precedent for this in organizations such as TVA, the New York Port Authority, and the Appalachia Commission.

Environmental process teams should be formed to serve as a team of professionals assisting the client in defining the problem; in analyzing and developing a program for action; in selecting a site; in making or directing the preparation of environmental design proposals; in building and evaluation of the demonstration area; and in formulating communication and educational procedures by which the demonstration can most effectively influence the improvement of the entire rural and urban fabric. Such environmental process study teams would be responsible for relating research results generally to the needs of growth and change, as well as to specific environmental interest, in demonstration sites.

10

Water

The earth's water is found in the seas (97%), in the polar ice caps (2%), and as fresh water (1%) (Wolman, 1962). Over 50 percent of the fresh water is stored as groundwater at depths of 2,500–12,500 feet (Table 27). Estimates of present and future national water needs, and availability for food and fiber production, include those published by Wolman (1962), Landsberg (1964), U.S. Water Resources Council (1968), Wollman and Bonem (1971), and Heady *et al.* (1972).

The average annual precipitation in the United States is approximately 30 inches or 4,750 million acre-feet (Wolman, 1962; Pavelis and Gertel, 1963; Todd, 1971) and is unlikely to change materially either quantitatively or spatially. Extensive use of desalinized water for agriculture is not predicted for the near future, and, in any discussion about the future of water resources, someone usually raises the issue of rainmaking.

An authoritative assessment of the feasibility of weather modification in the United States is to be found in the 1966 report by the National Research Council of the National Academy of Sciences (NAS–NRC) *Weather and Climate Modification, Problems and Prospects* (NAS, 1966b), which indicated that the time was nearly at hand when conditions

TABLE 27   Distribution of Fresh water

Location	Distribution (%)
Polar ice and glaciers	75
Groundwater (less than 2,500 ft)	11
Groundwater (2,500–12,500 ft)	14
Lakes	0.32
Rivers	0.03
Soil moisture	0.06
Atmosphere	0.035

SOURCE: (Wolman, 1962).

favorable to purposeful increase of rainfall could be predicted. This, in turn, led various people to begin examining secondary effects and debating whether weather change was really desirable. In 1968 "A National Program of Research in Agriculture for Weather Modification" was projected by the USDA and state experiment stations, giving equal emphasis to techniques for changing the weather and to assessment of the biological and hydrological consequences.

NAS–NRC is again examining the state of technology for weather modification and finds evidence of both positive and negative effects from seeding convective clouds. Evidence of rain modification from nonorographic, nonconvective clouds is meager. Possibilities of hail, hurricane, and lightning suppression are still attractive, but uncertain (Hammond, 1971).

To increase precipitation from cold orographic winter clouds seems nearest to realization. In the largest randomized seeding experiment in the United States involving this sort of cloud, it has been demonstrated that precipitation can be increased 10–30 percent. As a result, the Bureau of Reclamation has undertaken the largest precipitation modification experiment to date—an attempt to increase rainfall, and hence the runoff, in a 3,300-square-mile area in Colorado. The aim of the experiment is an average 16-percent increase in snowfall. Not surprisingly, the residents of the target region are not entirely happy with the prospects (Hammond, 1971).

Projections of water-resource changes resulting from weather modification are very difficult. A conservative view would seem to be that irrigation water from snow-clad mountains might be increased by a tenth by 1980; any other possibilities are too uncertain to be projected.

At least 97 percent of precipitation currently occurs on agricultural and forested land, including rangeland. The characteristics of these

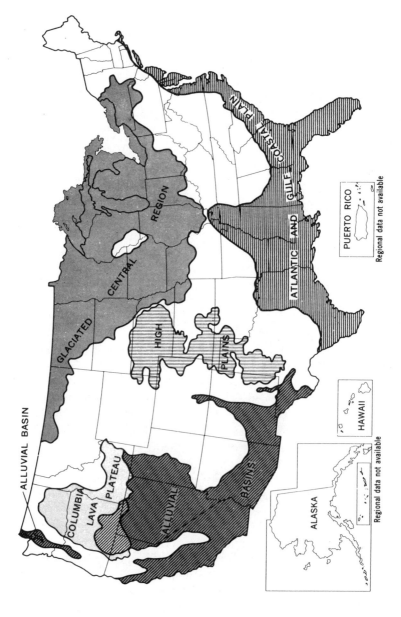

FIGURE 6 Average annual runoff in the United States (U.S. Water Resources Council, 1968).

lands (nature of the vegetation, etc.) and how they are used largely
determine the quality and quantity of water leaving the land. About
70 percent of precipitation on agricultural land is returned to the
atmosphere by evapotranspiration (USDA and State Universities and
Land Grant Colleges, 1969). The remaining 30 percent moves over the
land to streams, to lakes, to rivers, and on to the oceans. This average
annual runoff is shown by Figure 6. This runoff is either beneficial or
destructive, depending upon rates, volumes, and timing. The degree to
which surface flow causes soil erosion, floods, sedimentation, and
degradation of water is greatly influenced by agricultural and forestry
land use.

DEMAND

For planning purposes, the Water Resources Council has projected the
population to 245 million by 1980 (U.S. Water Resources Council,
1967). Water use has grown more rapidly in the past decades than has
the total economy. Although water use for irrigation has increased
substantially, agricultural production has grown at a lesser rate. The
growth of industries that require large quantities of water has been
more rapid than has the growth of total manufacturing. Household
water use has increased more rapidly than population. Per capita
urban use exceeds per capita rural use.

Dramatic population increases and industrial expansion are creating
some regional and local water shortages. During the next decade, some
areas are expected to experience a doubling of population. Changing
conditions in many places will accentuate existing water problems and
create new ones, as have rapid changes in the structure of American
society—especially a growing demand for water-based recreation facilities.
Industrial expansion in the densely populated East and elsewhere raises
serious doubt as to the feasibility of continuing to use rivers for industrial waste disposal. Increasing demands for water for agricultural production, recreation, fish and wildlife, household use, and transportation of wastes highlight the importance of attention to water allocation and water quality. These issues are most critical in water-short
areas, but they also demand attention elsewhere; they must be solved
if orderly growth and development of agriculture and industry is to continue with minimum insult to the environment.

The Water Resources Council (1968) has projected water supplies,
withdrawals and consumption for 18 river basins in the conterminous
United States. No regions are foreseen to be deficient by 2020. There
are a number, however—particularly the Upper Colorado and Lower

Colorado river basins—where consumption is expected to be more than 70 percent of the total available supply by 2020.

In a more recent study (Table 28), Wollman and Bonem calculated the total required flows (consumption) plus waste dilution and water available in 1960 and 2000 for 15 river basins in the United States (Wollman and Bonem, 1971). Water deficits were projected in four river basins for 2000, i.e., the Texas-Gulf, Rio Grande, Colorado and Great Basin. According to their study, these last three had a water deficit in 1960, along with the Lower Mississippi and California-South Pacific basins.

Estimates of gross and net use of water per acre for agriculture for 1960, 1980, 2000 and 2020 are shown in Table 29 from the same study. They projected a reduction in water loss per irrigated acre of about 20–35 percent in western regions, and a somewhat smaller change

TABLE 28   Total Water Consumption (Including Waste Dilution) and Water Available for 1960 and 2000 by River Basin as Reported in the Wollman–Bonem Study[a]

River Basin	1960			2000		
	Regulated Flow	Required Flow	Surplus or Deficit	Maximum Reg. Flow	Required Flow	Surplus or Deficit
Units: 1,000,000 acre-ft/yr						
North Atlantic	37.30	9.60	27.70	152.54	27.69	124.85
South Atlantic–Gulf	106.41	13.26	93.15	208.38	53.96	154.42
Great Lakes	13.78	9.44	4.34	71.20	28.56	42.64
Ohio	23.64	2.58	21.06	127.81	12.35	115.46
Tennessee	23.30	1.82	21.48	45.24	6.43	38.81
Upper Mississippi	17.70	2.07	15.63	51.67	5.96	45.71
Lower Mississippi	1.68	1.76	−0.08	39.44	5.95	33.49
Missouri[b]	34.72	14.97	19.75	46.83	22.22	24.61
Arkansas–White–Red	34.28	8.32	25.96	72.49	13.38	59.11
Texas–Gulf	17.25	13.85	3.40	29.01	29.96	−0.95
Rio Grande	3.36	5.59	−2.23	3.36	7.31	−3.95
Colorado[c]	12.77	16.20	−3.43	12.77	28.23	−15.46
Great Basin	6.05	6.45	−0.40	7.77	7.85	−0.08
Columbia–North Pacific	70.35	18.00	52.35	150.74	41.32	109.42
California–South Pacific	30.13	31.58	−1.45	51.86	47.70	4.16
United States	432.72	155.49	277.23	1,071.11	338.87	732.24

[a] Adapted from Table 82 (Wollman and Bonem, 1971). Assumes a medium level of economic growth and a minimum flow for waste dilution in the year 2000.
[b] Includes Souris–Red–Rainy flows and requirements.
[c] Includes Upper Colorado and Lower Colorado basins.

TABLE 29 Gross and Net Use of Water per Acre for Agriculture by River Basin

River Basin	1960		1980		2000		2020	
	With-drawal	Loss	With-drawal	Loss	With-drawal	Loss	With-drawal	Loss
Units: acre-ft/acre								
New England	0.8	0.8	0.8	0.7	0.8	0.7	0.8	0.7
Delaware and Hudson	1.1	1.0	1.0	0.9	0.9	0.8	0.9	0.8
Chesapeake Bay	1.4	1.3	1.3	1.2	1.2	1.1	1.2	1.1
Ohio River	1.4	1.3	1.3	1.2	1.2	1.1	1.2	1.1
Eastern Great Lakes	1.1	1.0	1.0	0.9	0.9	0.8	0.9	0.8
Western Great Lakes	1.4	1.3	1.3	1.2	1.2	1.1	1.2	1.1
Upper Mississippi River	1.7	1.5	1.5	1.4	1.4	1.3	1.4	1.3
Lower Missouri River	1.7	1.5	1.5	1.4	1.4	1.3	1.4	1.3
Southeast	1.8	1.7	1.7	1.6	1.6	1.5	1.6	1.5
Cumberland River	1.1	1.0	1.0	0.9	0.9	0.8	0.9	0.8
Tennessee River	1.2	1.2	1.2	1.1	1.1	1.0	1.1	1.0
Lower Mississippi River	1.9	1.8	1.8	1.6	1.7	1.6	1.7	1.6
Lower Arkansas–White–Red Rivers	1.8	1.7	1.6	1.5	1.5	1.4	1.5	1.4
Upper Missouri River	3.2	2.0	2.5	1.8	2.1	1.5	2.1	1.5
Upper Arkansas–White–Red Rivers	3.2	2.2	2.5	1.8	2.2	1.7	2.2	1.7
Western Gulf	2.7	1.8	2.1	1.5	1.8	1.4	1.8	1.4
Upper Rio Grande–Pecos Rivers	6.4	3.9	4.8	3.2	3.8	2.8	3.8	2.8
Colorado River	7.2	4.7	5.5	3.9	4.8	3.6	4.8	3.6
Great Basin	4.8	3.2	3.8	2.7	3.2	2.2	3.2	2.2
South Pacific	5.5	3.8	4.3	3.2	3.8	3.0	3.8	3.0
Central Pacific	5.4	3.7	4.7	3.3	4.0	3.0	4.0	3.0
Pacific Northwest	5.1	2.9	3.8	2.3	3.2	2.2	3.2	2.2

SOURCE: Table 11 (Wollman and Bonem, 1971). Published for Resources for the Future, Inc. by The Johns Hopkins University Press.

for eastern regions, between 1954 and 2000. In western regions, the net import of water per acre remained high: 4–5 acre-ft/acre for the Southwest and 2–2.5 acre-ft/acre for the Northwest.

The United States Geological Survey placed the proportion of water withdrawn for irrigation for the 50 states in 1965 at nearly 37.2 percent of a total of 347 million acre-feet withdrawn from ground and surface sources for all purposes.

Approximately 109 million acre-feet of water were used for irrigation in 1964. Rural homes, including farm homes, water for stock, and other farm uses accounted for only 4 million acre-feet (USDA and State Universities and Land Grant Colleges, 1969). In the 17 western states, about 80 percent of the water withdrawn is for irrigation. For the nation as a whole, about 315 billion gal/day, or a fourth of the water that reaches streams, is withdrawn. Less than one third of this water removed is actually consumed, the remaining two thirds returning to the streams. Approximately 96 percent of the consumed 100 billion gal/day is used by agriculture, and slightly less than 4 percent is used by industry and municipalities. Agriculture is clearly a major user of water (USDA and State Universities and Land Grant Colleges, 1969).

Water needed by agriculture depends greatly on the acreage under irrigation. Wollman and Bonem (1971) suggest that "to estimate the number of acres to receive irrigation in future years one must consider such factors as exports, national and regional demands, crop mix, regional distribution of agricultural activity, competing acres of land, prices paid by irrigators for irrigation water, the policies adopted by Congress for construction of water resource projects and direct allocation of water among competitive users." Three independent estimates of irrigated acres for 1980 are shown in Table 30.

Heady et al. (1972), in a recent computer simulation study, found that, if needed, considerable water might be released from agriculture for higher priority use by the year 2000. In this scheme, the amount of water and irrigated land employed in 2000 was determined within the context of a nationally optimum production and resource use pattern. Conclusions were that if exports did not increase substantially, the nation could have from 12.5 to 51 million more acres of crop- and hay land than would be needed to meet food and fiber needs in the year 2000. Also, irrigated land in the year 2000 could be reduced 9.4–26.1 million acres below the 1969 level. The impact of government subsidy programs on the price of water and the substitutability of water for other production inputs (such as fertilizer) was pointed out; government

TABLE 30 Estimated United States Acres under Irrigation (1980)

Forecast Source	Acres under Irrigation—1980 (millions)		
	Total	Eastern U.S.	Western U.S.
Ruttan, 1965	49.7	12.4	37.4
Pavelis, 1965[a]	43.2	4.1	39.1
USDA, 1960[b]	56.7	3.7	33.0

[a] Pavelis, G. A., "Irrigation Policy and Long-term Growth Functions." *ERS-USDA Agricultural Economics Research* 17(2):50-60 (April, 1965).
[b] (U.S. 86th Congress, 1st Session, 1960).

programs to develop more irrigated land were shown to be in conflict with those that pay farmers to leave land idle in other parts of the country. Many of these same ideas were advanced several years earlier (NAS, 1968a).

Water is used in agriculture in the United States according to procedures and techniques developed by the Bureau of Reclamation, the Bureau of Land Management, the USDA's Forest Service and Agricultural Research Service, the state agricultural experiment stations, private research organizations and individual land managers. Early efforts to develop agriculture and water resources in arid sections of the United States frequently failed because soil–plant–water relations in arid environments were inadequately understood. Fortunately, information about proper management of soil-water and crops has accumulated rapidly enough to sustain an irrigation agriculture that contributes about 20 percent of the total food and fiber of this nation, with minimum adverse effect on the environment (Thorne, 1970). Of course, there are specific locations where poor judgment, shortsighted planning or mismanagement have resulted in irreparable damage to land and water resources. Fortunately, there are few such instances, and similar mistakes should be infrequent as new technology in irrigation agriculture is applied. It is imperative that continuing research be carried out to improve water management in irrigation agriculture, looking to increased efficiency, runoff control, evaporation suppression, salt control and crop production in arid areas.

QUALITY

Because agriculture is a major user of water and has substantial potential to pollute water supplies with sediment, animal wastes, plant nutrients and other chemicals, it is as subject to public scrutiny and controls as is any other user with which it must compete. Wastes and chemicals were considered in an earlier chapter; sediments will be discussed here.

Practically all natural rivers carry sediment, largely as the product of erosion. In toto, the losses of soil are enormous. By no means all sediment is the result of human action.

If man had never intervened, most rivers would carry large quantities of sediment. Consider, for example, data provided by Pecora (1971) on three United States rivers: Prior to the construction of upstream dams, the Colorado River carried approximately 40,000 tons of sediment per day into Lake Mead, from a watershed that was relatively free of encroachment. The Mississippi River carries an average of more than 2 million tons of sediment daily—equivalent to the load of 40,000 freight cars—into the Gulf of Mexico. And the Paria River, with head-waters in Bryce Canyon, carries about 500 times as much sediment per unit volume of water as does the Mississippi River. Rivers in their natural state also transport enormous loads of dissolved solids. The Brazos River in Texas, for example, transports 25,000 tons of dissolved salt per day, mostly from natural sources. Finally, it is clear that the balance between water flow and sediment load is important in the evolution of river channels. The slope and cross section of a river is such as to permit the river to transport the average imposed sediment load with the available water discharge. If the sediment load becomes disproportionately large, deposition will occur in the upland regions and the channel will broaden to produce higher flow velocities and increased flow-bed contact area (both of which increase the sediment carrying ability of a stream). By the same token, any activity that alters the water or sediment discharge of a river will induce changes downstream.

Although natural hydrologic processes cause extensive erosion, many of man's activities greatly increase it. For example, a watershed study in Maryland (Guy, 1963) revealed that, during the construction accompanying urbanization, an additional 10 tons of sediment per new inhabitant were delivered to the stream that drained the area. Construction of highways and other large projects also greatly increases erosion rates. According to the Joint Task Force on Pollution in Relation to Forestry and Agriculture (USDA, 1968d), erosion caused by surface runoff is by far the dominant form of soil loss in the United States, delivering approximately 4 billion tons/yr of sediment to waterways in the 48 contiguous states. This report also states that about three fourths of this comes from agricultural lands. Water erosion is severe on 179 million acres of croplands and significant on an additional 50 million acres. It was also estimated that the suspended solids transported to United States streams by surface runoff are at least 700-times those imposed by sewage discharge.

Agriculture increases the rate of surface runoff erosion for several reasons. Most cropping systems entail removing the natural vegetative cover and pulverizing the soil periodically; thus, these systems increase the quantity and erosive capacity of runoff and reduce soil moisture. Table 31 (American Society of Civil Engineers, 1962) compares erosion and surface runoff under natural precipitation for five different regions. The 4 billion tons of erosion produced annually by surface runoff corresponds to an average loss of approximately 2 tons/acre, but it is distributed unevenly across the United States, being relatively small in areas of dense natural vegetation and large in tilled areas.

TABLE 31 Annual Soil and Water Losses per Acre from Five Widely Separated Types of Land Under Conditions of Clean Tillage and Dense Cover of Vegetation[a]

Soil, Location, and Years of Measurements	Average Annual Precipitation (in.)	Slope (%)	Clean-Tilled Crop		Dense Cover–Thick-Growing Crop		Approximate Number of Years to Remove 7-in. of Soil	
			Annual Soil Loss[b] (tons)	Annual Water Loss[c] (%)	Annual Soil Loss[b] (ton)	Annual Water Loss[c] (%)	Clean Tillage	Dense Cover
Shelby silt loam, Bethany, Mo., 1931–1935	34.79	8	68.78	28.31	0.29	9.30	16	3,900
Kirvin fine sandy loam, Tyler, Tex., 1931–1936	40.82	8.75	27.95	20.92	0.124	1.15	49	11,100
Vernon fine sandy loam, Guthrie, Okla., 1930–1935	33.01	7.7	24.29	14.22	0.032	1.23	50	33,200
Marshall silt loam, Clarinda, Iowa, 1933–1935	26.82	9	18.82	8.64	0.06	0.97	48	15,200
Cecil clay loam, Statesville, N. C., 1931–1935	45.22	10	22.58	10.21	0.012	0.33	51	95,800

SOURCE: Table 2-C.1, p. 111 (American Society of Civil Engineers, 1962).

[a] Measurements at the soil and water conservation experiment stations of the Soil Conservation Service.

[b] Based on actual volume–weight determinations of the several soils as follows: Shelby silt loam 1.43, Kirvin fine sandy loam 1.73, Vernon fine sandy loam 1.54, Marshall silt loam 1.15, Cecil clay loam 1.45 g/ml.

[c] Of total precipitation.

TABLE 32   Possible Reduction of Soil Erosion on Nine Illinois Reservoir
Watersheds

Reservoir	Watershed Area (sq mile)	Annual Sediment Deposition Rate (ton/acre)	Computed Soil Loss from Watershed (ton/acre)		Reduction of Soil Loss by Conservation (%)
			Present Condition	After Conservation Program	
Ridge Lake	1.41	4.36	4.36	1.87	43
Lake Carthage	2.90	2.50	3.80	1.03	73
Carbondale Reservoir	3.10	7.68	11.6	.95	92
West Frankfort Reservoir	4.03	4.00	4.36	.65	85
Lake Bracken	9.14	3.37	7.02	.78	89
Lake Calhoun	13.1	2.00	8.27	.91	89
Spring Lake	20.2	1.44	4.55	.88	81
Crab Orchard Lake	196	2.80	5.37	.51	91
Lake Springfield	258	1.03	3.26	.72	78

SOURCE: (Stall, 1962), p. 126.

Although agriculture almost inevitably increases the sediment from an area, the increase can be greatly reduced by proper practices. Measures that reduce soil loss include proper tillage and contouring, maintenance of high fertility, mulching, terracing, and crop rotation. A rather thorough discussion of these and other measures and their effectiveness is available in Meyer and Mannering (1967). The estimated reductions in erosion that could be achieved in sample watersheds by reasonable soil conservation measures are summarized in Table 32 (Stall, 1962).

There are at least two indirect consequences of soil conservation practices. First, measures that reduce erosion generally also decrease surface runoff, and hence the surface-water yield of the area. Indeed, it is the runoff reduction that is principally responsible for the diminished erosion. This is not altogether a net loss of water, however, since soil moisture and groundwater reserves are enhanced by the increased infiltration. Second, reduced soil loss is accompanied by a decrease in the amounts of herbicides, insecticides, and fertilizer that are transported to lakes and rivers. Many of these chemicals are absorbed on soil particles and move with the sediment.

ALLOCATING WATER AND CONTROLLING QUALITY

Public policy regarding water quality has been evolving since 1948 when the first temporary water pollution control legislation was passed. The

Federal Water Pollution Control Act of 1956 was the first permanent legislation. It authorized planning, technical assistance, grants for state programs, and grants for construction of municipal waste treatment facilities. Amendments in 1961 extended federal enforcement authority and increased construction grant authorization (Council on Environmental Quality, 1970).

The water quality standards authorized by 1965 legislation establishing the Federal Water Pollution Control Administration set the stage for the current strategy of water quality management. This act required each state to establish standards for their interstate waters and to secure approval from the Secretary of the Interior. To set these standards, states had to consider carefully present and potential uses of water and establish standards necessary to provide for them. Specific plans for achieving these quality levels in each state have subsequently been developed. Most states, working with the Environmental Protection Agency, are rapidly evolving enforcement procedures to ensure that water quality standards are met by all users.

Historically, public policy on water in the United States has supported national economic efficiency through income maximization (James *et al.,* 1969). The issuance in June, 1969, of the "Procedures for Evaluation of Water and Related Land Resource Projects" (U.S. Water Resources Council, 1969) by the Special Task Force of the Water Resources Council set in motion water development plans to consider not only national income, but also regional development, environmental quality and social well-being.

The adoption of multi-objective standards for evaluating water development projects has long-range implications for agriculture that necessitate the development of revised principles for planning water resource uses (U.S. Water Resources Council, 1970a). Standards must be developed that permit consistent and equitable decisions regarding development and allocation of water for agricultural production (U.S. Water Resources Council, 1970b).

Since water availability, quality and demand vary regionally, research and detailed planning for development and use should be regionalized [Kerr Committee Report (U.S. 86th Congress, 1960); Wolman, 1962; Landsberg, 1964]. Local and regional plans, quality standards, and usage must be compatible with principles and standards accepted nationally (NAS, 1966a, 1968a).

Although multi-objective approaches to water- and land-use planning are praiseworthy, effective implementation will be difficult. It will no longer be possible to place projects in an unambiguous priority list. There is increased likelihood of confusion and manipulation by special interests. This approach will be extremely difficult and ineffective without a vigorous continuing research program providing a foundation of knowledge about all related topics (Wolman, 1962).

The competitive position of agriculture in the race for limited water supplies is poor. A given supply of water, if there are scarcities, will create much more economic activity if used by industry than by agriculture. The effects of a given water policy on agriculture and its ability to meet the demands for production of food and fiber cannot be accurately assessed, until the constraints on development and use of water for agriculture are elucidated, and some experience has accumulated. It is clear, however, that any policy that makes water for irrigation expensive, relegates irrigation to low priority, or places unrealistic standards of quality on effluent from agricultural land will disrupt food and fiber production. Agriculture's competitive position must be improved by research upon water-use efficiency, the disruptions by reallocation of water must be gauged ahead of the change (e.g. Heady *et al.*, 1972), and people must be compensated whenever they are injured by changes in water policy made in the name of "national interest."

11

Energy

Rural America is important both as a supplier and a user of energy; a shortage of readily available energy in rural areas is a potentially important limiting factor to food production and to rural growth. If rural areas are to be made competitive with suburban areas as desirable places for living, then energy—especially electricity—must be provided to these areas at a reasonable cost. Also, energy in the form of electricity and mobile fuel is necessary in large quantities for the advancing technologies that enhance the efficient production of food.

DEMANDS AND AVAILABILITY

Energy (as gas, liquid and solid fossil fuels) consumed directly or indirectly as electric power is an integral and essential input for modern agriculture in the field, the processing plant, movement of materials and farm products and the manufacture of supplies (chemical, machinery, etc.). It is estimated that agriculture and its ancillary industries require from 7-10 percent of the total energy demand of the entire United States. A 50 percent increase in energy consumption by agriculture is projected on the basis of a United States population estimate of 300 million people by 2000 and an increase in energy consumption per capita. This estimate may well be conservative, as it depends heavily on expected

151

population changes and allows for only slight increases in per capita consumption of energy for food and fiber production. Taking the 1968 total United States annual energy demand at 62 × 10¹⁵ BTU, agriculture consumes approximately 6 × 10¹⁵ BTU. This can therefore be expected to reach about 9–10 × 10¹⁵ BTU by the year 2000.

On the basis of some eight variously estimated total United States energy requirements for year 2000 (Table 33), 9–10 × 10¹⁵ BTU would comprise from 5–10 percent of the nation's energy supply, a figure which appears to be within reasonable limits of error.

Although electric power consumption on the farm has enormously increased over the past 30 years and will probably continue to rise over the next thirty (at least as much as industrial use, i.e., about sixfold over present farm consumption), the major increase in absolute use of farm energy is expected to be in gas and liquid fuels, primarily for mobile equipment and transport.

The major increases in consumption of farm energy, geographically, will coincide with the production increases of the major agricultural regions. These can be estimated, in descending order, as the North Central, Southeast, South Central, Northwest, Pacific Coast, Southwest and Northeast.

Overall, the United States annual demand for energy rose at the rate of 3.1%/yr over the period 1950–1970 and may well accelerate to nearly a 4%/yr increment by 2000. In 1968, United States total energy consumption (62 × 10¹⁵ BTU, or $20 billion) comprised 36 percent of the total world supply. As emerging nations seek increasingly to industrial-

TABLE 33   Forecasts of United States Total Energy Requirements, 1970–2000

Forecast Source	Base Value, Year	Energy Requirements (BTU × 10¹⁵)		Average Annual Growth Rate (%)
		1980	2000	
Putnam, 1953	33 (1950)	87.6	148.2	3.0
Searl, 1960	42.9(1959)	86.2	170.0	3.4
Weeks, 1960	–	92.0	187.0	3.6
U.S. Atomic Energy Commission, 1962	44.9(1960)	67.0	101.0	2.1
Landsberg et al., 1963	45.4(1960)	79.2	135.2	2.8
Sporn, 1963	44.9(1960)	70.7[a]	104.8	2.1
U.S. Atomic Energy Commission, 1966	–	80.0	130.0	2.5
Morrison and Readling, 1968	53.8(1965)	88.1	168.6	–

[a] Projection is for 1975.

ize and mechanize their food and fiber production, it is probable the United States percentage consumption of total world energy output will decline. It is estimated that the abundance of conventional energy fuels throughout the world can meet all foreseeable world demands through 2000 and beyond. However, although the United States has ample resources of indigenous supplies of proved fossil fuels to meet all anticipated demands through 2000 and for at least 50 years beyond at the anticipated consumption rates 30 years from now, the total United States fossil energy supply is not particularly reassuring. The bulk of the fossil energy resource is coal (chiefly bituminous), which cannot be readily employed as an energy source for agriculture.

Table 34 gives the estimated range of fossil fuel "proved" reserves within United States territories. When the anticipated annual demands for both oil and gas combined are weighed against the combined estimated reserves, the data are disturbing:

Year	Range	Anticipated Demand[a] (BTU $\times 10^{15}$)	Estimated Reserves[b] (BTU $\times 10^{15}$)	Ratio Years Supply
2000	Low	76.6	522	6.81
	High	148.0	815	5.51

[a] (USDI, 1970).
[b] (Morrison and Readling, 1968).

Although hydrocarbon fuels comprise 96 percent of the United States total energy supply at the present time, it is anticipated that new technologies will evolve new sources of power. These developments include nuclear energy, particularly fusion; oil from shale and coal; and gas from coal and lignite.

Table 35 gives estimates of these energy resources, which, if based on actual 1968 consumption, would provide a total energy supply for 561 years; however, for the "low" and "high" estimates of consumption in the year 2000 the supply would extend for 242 and 156 years, respectively. Such estimates, though deemed feasible, nevertheless hinge upon technologies yet to be evolved and reduced to practice, some of which may constitute a serious insult to the environment—e.g., strip-mining and radioactive residues.

It can safely be concluded that energy demands for agriculture through year 2000 can be readily supplied, although it is highly probable the input cost will substantially increase.

TABLE 34 Estimated Range of Proved United States Reserves of Fossil Fuel

Resource (eq units)	Range	U.S. Reserves (BTU × 10¹⁵)		
		1965	1980	2000
Coal	Low		5,764	5,764
(1 ton = 26.2 × 10⁶ BTU)	Med	5,764	7,493	8,253
	High		9,248	10,742
Natural gas (dry)	Low		296	296
(1 cu ft = 1035 BTU)	Med	296	381	530
	High		456	765
Crude oil + NGL	Low		226	226
(1 barrel = 5.8 × 10⁶ BTU)	Med	226	296	486
	High		359	516
TOTALS	Low		6,286	6,286
	Med		8,170	9,269
	High		10,063	12,023
Estimated demands	Low		73.9(85)[a]	106.5(59)
	Med		88.1(93)[a]	168.6(55)
	High		104.7(96)[a]	209.4(57)

SOURCE: (Morrison and Readling, 1968).
[a] Figures in parentheses are years of use relating estimated demands to estimated reserves.

TABLE 35 Estimates of United States Energy Resources From All Fuels

Energy Resource	Quantity	Units	Equivalent Units (BTU × 10¹⁵)
Fossil			
Coal (anthracite)	6,845	megatons × 10⁶	174
Coal (bituminous)	773,453	megatons × 10⁶	20,252
Petroleum	532	barrels × 10⁹	3,086
Natural Gas	2,400	cu ft × 10¹²	2,484
Bituminous oil	4	barrels × 10⁹	23
Shale oil	80	barrels × 10⁹	464
SUBTOTAL			26,483
Fissile			
Uranium	552,500	megatons	325[a]
Thorium	527,000	megatons	2,901
SUBTOTAL			3,226
TOTAL			29,709

SOURCE: (USDI, 1970).
[a] Theoretical BTU equivalent 39 × 10¹⁸.

SITING OF ENERGY PRODUCTION FACILITIES

The history of the electric utility industry has been to keep abreast of growing demand. Small generating plants located in and surrounded by their load areas have given way to larger, more efficient but more remote plants, often interconnected by high-voltage transmission lines.

The electric industry places its hydro plants on rivers in accordance with the availability of economical sites. Thermal plants are most often located near rivers, often closer to load and fuel supply. Nuclear plants also need cooling water, but can be remote from their fuel sources. High-voltage transmission lines then link these generating plants with the load and with each other, often with some redundant lines to assure reliability. The time is long past when these plants and lines can be located without regard to their impact on life-support systems and on esthetic considerations.

Since generating plants are almost always built to satisfy an obvious need, they cannot be said to accelerate the growth of electric load. But failure to construct a facility, in violation of a utility's responsibility, can retard the growth that the facility was to serve.

It is seldom that a generating plant will inhibit industrial development in its immediate area; often residential growth will occur. A thermal power plant, with adequate control of particulate and gaseous emissions and noise, appropriately separated by a greenbelt and landscaping, is hardly a bad neighbor either to industry or housing.

Since it must be acknowledged that a power plant is a less desirable neighbor than a park or another house, once the general area for a plant site is selected, it is wise to look to other compatible uses that will make for optimum area development. For instance, a modern incinerator might occupy a nearby area and thus make its waste heat useful for power generation. Heated effluent from the plant might be used for irrigation or as a first stage in desalination. More effort and cooperation must be devoted to this useful concept, sharing of rights-of-way. Natural gas and oil pipelines, telephone cables, water and sewage pipelines, railroads, and even highway routes all have potential for utilizing a common corridor.

Transmission line corridors through undeveloped areas often can provide greenbelt separation for future urban and suburban development. These corridors could be left in their natural state for trails and wildlife habitat or made into park and recreation areas. In urban areas they often can be used for parking and for access corridors. The rights-of-way offer little impediment to agriculture or pastureland except under the towers themselves, but they are not compatible with the growth of most forest products, except Christmas tree production, perhaps.

Land use may be affected by esthetic consideration. In the case of power plants and transmission lines, there is no general agreement even among experts as to what constitutes a pleasing structure. Many of the so-called outdoor power plants have been regarded favorably by some modern architects. Lattice-type transmission towers are functionally correct and, in many applications, are often much less obtrusive on a scenic vista than some of the more expensive, heavy, pipe-type structures finding acceptance in other locations.

The "low profile" substation or one using box girder takeoff structures will find application in urban environments but may be unnecessary where the substation can be sufficiently screened.

Optimum land use is always of paramount importance. The added plant sites and transmission corridors required by increasing electrical loads must fit with the best possible utilization pattern of our existing land resource to achieve an optimum balance among diverse existing and potential land uses. Some, like Lewis and McHarg (Lewis, 1969; McHarg, 1969; Hall–Kane Associates and Landscapes, Inc., 1970), have developed methods of identifying such uses and compatibilities. However, studies based on these methods must include only those variables truly associated with siting conditions, which then must be given a scale of importance commensurate with their optimum public value. For example, one of the variables that must be considered in routing a transmission line is the necessity for suitable soil conditions to provide reliable tower foundations. This could dictate use of the more stable ridge lines, even though such routes may violate rigid esthetic criteria.

The public must always be brought into the planning process. The appropriate point, however, is often hard to establish. Several alternative plant sites or line routes should be available for consideration; yet these must be sufficiently tentative to permit genuine give and take. It will usually not be possible to get full concurrence from all people who are immediately affected, even under the best of circumstances.

Effect of Elimination of the Use of Fragile Lands for Production of Food and Fiber

Precise information is needed on the environmental, and the dollar, cost and on the potential to meet food needs of an increasing population under alternative choices of resource allocation. Data banks, reliable coefficients for selected variables, estimates of population density, and of the interrelationships of food and the environment need to be established, updated and tested for accuracy and application to real situations.

As examples of environmental insult, the Committee considered subjecting to analysis the production, acreage and cost influence of decreasing total fertilizer input coupled with associated crop, soil and climate variables. They also considered altered pesticide practices on a preventative or as-needed basis, the effect of feed additives on meat production and the influence of reserving fragile lands for nonagricultural production. Sufficient funds were not available for extensive analytical examples. Thus, the Committee selected one variable for specific study— land, in its capacity to feed the United States population in the year 2000 (based on a population estimate of 280 million). The results were computed under the restriction of removing all fragile lands from agricultural production. In view of the growing awareness of need for planning and for predictive values, this appendix and calculations are offered as examples, not as a cure-all.

The Committee worked with the Center for Agricultural and Rural

Development at Iowa State University in adapting Model B from the NWC Report (Heady *et al.,* 1972) to accommodate a fragile land constraint. As explained earlier Model B consisted of (1) free market conditions, (2) current water prices, (3) agricultural exports projected at the 1967–1969 base in 2000, (4) a production technology trend projected from the period 1920–1970, and (5) a projected population of 280 million in the United States in the year 2000.

Model A, not subjected to analyses, assumed the United States population at 300 million in the year 2000. This base was not used in the present computations because preliminary estimates suggested that an extensive computer reiteration would be required, for which funds were not currently available, and that production to feed this population would not be achieved unless a number of adjustments in land use and activities were realized. This analysis, termed Model F, was constructed by starting with Model B (Heady *et al.,* 1972) and adding as a constraint the removal of fragile lands from agricultural production. The details of the computation are available from the Center for Agricultural and Rural Development, Iowa State University. The data are summarized for the Water Resources Council's 18 river basins for dryland acreages, and for the 9 western river basins for irrigated acreages.

Fragile lands, for the present computation, were defined as areas in which extensive use or application to purposes at variance with their natural characteristics would cause them to deteriorate rapidly and require excessive input to maintain the new usage. This category includes the blow lands, wash lands and wetlands on which agricultural uses would be predicted to affect the quality of water, air, vegetation cover, wildlife and other natural resources within a particular biome. The Committee undertook this particular analysis to demonstrate both the method and necessity of analyses of the possible consequences resulting from the alteration of variables that affect the environment and agricultural productivity of a given area in a differential and conflicting manner.

Empirically, the fragile lands are interpreted to include the soils and areas of land capability, Classes V–VIII, using the year 1967 data from the United States Department of Agriculture national inventory of soil and water conservation.* As this USDA report states, soils of Classes VI, VII and VIII are generally not suitable for growing ordinary field crops. In addition to removing soil Classes V–VIII from agricultural use, Class IV lands in the High Plains area were shifted from crop produc-

---

* Conservation Needs Inventory Committee of the U.S. Department of Agriculture, *National Inventory of Soil and Water Conservation Needs, 1967.* Statistical Bulletin No. 461. U.S. Government Printing Office, Washington, D.C., 1971.

tion to hay and pasture in the interest of stabilizing soils from blowing. The Class IV lands to be reserved for hay and pasture are listed in Appendix Table A1. The land-capability class data has been expanded from sample areas to a county inventory by the Statistical Laboratory, Iowa State University, and the Data Processing Center, Texas A. & M. University.† All data are stored by counties on magnetic tape within the files of the Survey Group, Statistical Laboratory, Iowa State University. The Committee is indebted to this group for aid in the analysis including the transfer of the data from magnetic tape to the computer.

The computation of acreages needed for the production of grain, silage, hay and pasture are contained in Tables A2–A5; the data for the 18 river basins, Tables A2 and A3; for the irrigated acreages, Tables A4 and A5. The computations of the annual crop and livestock production are carried in Tables A6 and A7, and feed utilization figures for the various meat, egg and milk production livestock are given in Table A8. Projection of the average prices received by farmers in the year 2000 under Models A, B and F are tabulated in Table A9, together with the actual values for 1969. It must be recalled that the 1969 data are influenced by a land-retirement program of about 50 million acres. The three projected computations—A, B and F—are calculated on free land use. It should be recalled that Model A is without restriction for the 300 million population, B is for 280 million and Model F is for the 280 million population for the year 2000 with fragile lands removed from agricultural use. According to these computations, the unit cost differential between Models B and F is considerably greater for some products than for others. For example, the cost to cotton is unaffected, the increase for barley and oats is minimal, whereas the cost for corn-sorghum and soybeans is appreciable in percentage as is the hay and silage production cost.

If a population projection of 300 million were incorporated with the restraint of Model F, the prices of these crops and of livestock would have been higher—the cost increases were tentatively estimated to approach twice the values calculated with the 280 million base calculation.

These conclusions suggest both methods and data whereby tradeoffs may be determined in the decision-making processes to resolve conflicts between environmental quality and the need to produce food and fiber. The Committee concludes that the projected food and fiber requirements for the year 2000 A.D. can be met but at higher than current prices. The price level will be affected by constraints upon agricultural production

---

† For details on inventory procedures, see USDA Statistical Bulletin No. 461, *op. cit.*, Appendices I, II and III, pp. 203-211.

occasioned by efforts to improve the quality of the environment. The levels of environmental quality to be sought and achieved will very likely be markedly affected by both the availability and the prices of food and fiber under the practices proposed. It is recommended that legislative and administrative policy makers be knowledgeable in the major consequences of their policy decisions in an *ex ante,* rather than in an *ex post,* time frame.

TABLE A1   Resource Areas: Class IV
Land Considered as "Fragile"

No.	Area[a]
58	Northern Rolling High Plains
60	Pierre Shale Plains and Badlands
61	Black Hills Foot Slopes
62	Black Hills
64	Mixed Sandy and Silty Tableland
65	Nebraska Sand Hills
66	Dakota–Nebraska Eroded Tableland
67	Central High Plains
68	Irrigated Upper Platte River Valley
69	Upper Arkansas Valley Rolling Plains
70	Pecos–Canadian Plains and Valleys
71	Central Nebraska Loess Hills
72	Central High Tableland
73	Rolling Hills and Breaks
77	Southern High Plains
78	Central Rolling Red Plains
79	Great Bend Sand Plains

[a] From Soil Conservation Service map 1968, "Major Land Resource Areas of the United States." [See Agriculture Handbook 296 (USDA, 1965a).]

TABLE A2   Annual Crops on Dryland Acreages, Year 2000 Projection on Model F (Fragile Lands of 18 River Basins Unused)

River Basin	Total Acreage (1,000 acres)		Acreage Projection by Crop for 2000 (1,000 acres)							
	1964[a]	2000	Wheat	Corn Grain	Grain Sorghum	Oats	Barley	Soybeans	Cotton	Sugar Beets
New England	37	83	0	0	0	83	0	0	0	0
Middle Atlantic	3,671	4,963	2,838	0	0	0	2,125	0	0	0
South Atlantic–Gulf	10,084	9,703	197	0	903	0	1,444	7,159	0	37
Great Lakes	10,513	11,921	2,444	3,794	0	1,875	121	3,650	0	0
Ohio	16,020	18,886	2,432	9,940	0	1,102	0	5,412	0	0
Tennessee	1,215	1,067	0	0	0	0	0	0	1,067	0
Upper Mississippi	37,849	36,899	3,696	15,106	2,695	2,644	0	12,758	0	0
Lower Mississippi	11,154	14,017	5,324	0	0	0	0	5,835	2,858	0
Souris–Red–Rainy	9,317	9,028	1,353	1,158	0	6,517	0	0	0	0
Missouri	43,416	30,641	9,741	1,129	6,003	4,586	1,179	8,003	0	0
Arkansas–White–Red	18,929	13,030	9,464	1,390	711	477	378	610	0	0
Texas–Gulf	8,512	11,529	2,234	20	7,590	1,184	501	0	0	0
Rio Grande	374	970	0	0	970	0	0	0	0	0
Upper Colorado	167	46	46	0	0	0	0	0	0	0
Lower Colorado	21	0	0	0	0	0	0	0	0	0
Great Basin	320	391	303	0	0	41	47	0	0	0
Columbia–North Pacific	4,686	5,824	4,254	0	0	681	0	0	0	889
California–South Pacific	94	1,492	159	0	925	128	280	0	0	0
TOTAL (United States)	176,379	170,490	44,485	32,537	19,797	19,318	6,075	43,427	3,925	926

[a] U.S. Dept. of Commerce, Bureau of the Census, *U.S. Census of Agriculture, 1964.* Vol. 2, General Report. Washington, D.C., 1968.

161

TABLE A3   Annual Dryland Acreages as in Table A2: Silages, Hay and Pasture

	Acreage per Crop (1,000 acres)							
	Silages		Hay (Tame)		Hay (Wild)		Pasture	
River Basin	1964	2000	1964	2000	1964	2000	1964ᵃ	2000ᵇ
New England	138	0	1,031	0	0	0	1,551	722
Middle Atlantic	1,041	0	4,289	0	0	0	8,234	5,569
South Atlantic–Gulf	370	794	1,675	1,498	0	0	30,314	31,214
Great Lakes	1,402	818	5,356	7,330	35	26	7,256	7,777
Ohio	639	444	5,603	5,077	0	0	21,570	12,629
Tennessee	102	0	1,025	1,586	0	0	5,658	2,606
Upper Mississippi	2,786	3,773	8,785	16,362	357	308	21,150	14,533
Lower Mississippi	121	0	957	1,209	43	40	12,137	15,923
Souris–Red–Rainy	425	1,134	1,282	3,733	771	647	4,224	2,648
Missouri	2,716	3,877	10,548	28,610	6,234	4,983	169,015	71,598
Arkansas–White–Red	546	1,232	2,819	12,070	1,201	1,002	79,262	43,564
Texas–Gulf	108	231	1,387	3,275	141	96	71,139	50,290
Rio Grande	7	0	32	289	5	2	52,276	10,900
Upper Colorado	9	0	68	806	10	7	15,449	3,402
Lower Colorado	2	0	2	0	1	0	44,995	38,000
Great Basin	34	261	127	133	31	26	16,371	6,249
Columbia–North Pacific	122	85	1,373	1,430	139	128	35,555	18,897
California–South Pacific	4	0	316	0	37	35	25,036	12,427
TOTAL (U.S.)	10,572	12,649	46,675	83,408	9,005	7,300	621,192	348,948

NOTE: 1964 data from same source as in Table A2.
ᵃ Without public grazing lands.
ᵇ With public grazing lands: 291 million acres.

TABLE A4 Annual Crops on Irrigated Acreages: Year 2000 Projections on Model F (Fragile Land of 9 Western River Basins Unused)

River Basin	Total Acreage (1,000 acres)		Acreage Projection by Crop for 2000 (1,000 acres)							
	1964[a]	2000	Wheat	Corn Grain	Grain Sorghum	Oats	Barley	Soy-beans	Cotton	Sugar Beets
Missouri	2,021	799	113	398	31	257	0	0	0	0
Arkansas-White-Red	1,568	1,895	0	289	1,545	15	0	8	38	0
Texas-Gulf	2,764	855	0	52	735	30	0	0	38	0
Rio Grande	755	240	0	0	179	10	0	0	51	0
Upper Colorado	86	104	0	48	0	56	0	0	0	0
Lower Colorado	661	312	0	0	0	0	312	0	0	0
Great Basin	222	195	67	99	0	0	91	0	0	37
Columbia-North Pacific	918	1,114	979	60	0	36	0	0	0	0
California-South Pacific	2,247	1,015	364	60	95	12	130	0	289	65
TOTAL (Western basins)	11,242	6,529	1,523	946	2,585	416	533	8	416	102

NOTE: 1964 data from same source as in Table A2.

163

TABLE A5 Irrigated Acreages as Table A4: Silages, Hay, Pasture, plus Fruits, Nuts, Rice and Vegetables

Acreage per Crop (1,000 acres)

River Basin	Silages		Hay (Tame)		Hay (Wild)		Pasture		Fruits, Nuts, Rice, Vegetables	
	1964	2000	1964	2000	1964	2000	1964	2000	1964	2000
Missouri	301	461	1,345	2,994	459	307	984	818	34	40
Arkansas–White–Red	86	260	226	363	16	11	145	125	22	34
Texas–Gulf	35	43	72	36	0	0	237	168	534	468
Rio Grande	29	48	286	210	58	53	268	204	227	110
Upper Colorado	15	55	532	203	174	122	580	459	66	5
Lower Colorado	36	0	229	179	4	0	101	54	141	118
Great Basin	5	0	547	391	293	265	499	260	33	67
Columbia–North Pacific	93	85	1,596	2,586	291	163	1,147	1,175	621	777
California–South Pacific	145	89	1,317	2,332	66	7	1,132	1,022	2,418	2,766
TOTAL (Western basins)	745	1,041	6,150	9,294	1,361	928	5,093	4,285	4,096	4,385

NOTE: 1964 data from same source as in Table A2.

164

TABLE A6 Annual Crop Production: Year 2000 Projection on Model F (Fragile Lands of 18 River Basins Unused)

River Basin	Grain (1,000 bushels)			Silage (1,000 tons)[c]	Oilmeal (1,000 cwt)[d]
	Wheat	Corn and Sorghum[a]	Barley[b] and Oats	Corn and Sorghum	Soybeans and Cottonseed
New England	0	0	4,547	0	0
Middle Atlantic	130,088	0	137,543	0	0
South Atlantic–Gulf	10,922	73,600	115,581	12,885	122,188
Great Lakes	130,814	407,484	147,695	13,844	60,799
Ohio	118,648	1,167,764	71,859	8,298	103,830
Tennessee	0	0	0	0	5,847
Upper Mississippi	224,709	2,169,012	145,420	74,584	233,114
Lower Mississippi	264,602	0	0	0	127,964
Souris–Red–Rainy	57,436	65,813	449,999	12,735	0
Missouri	377,986	718,768	350,204	65,415	133,144
Arkansas–White–Red	283,862	419,843	25,376	39,413	14,987
Texas–Gulf	63,459	453,591	33,221	6,380	291
Rio Grande	0	70,719	525	1,864	402
Upper Colorado	1,308	5,557	2,876	2,040	0
Lower Colorado	0	0	27,097	0	0
Great Basin	11,335	0	10,307	6,164	0
Columbia–North Pacific	361,983	13,303	35,651	6,355	0
California–South Pacific	44,791	110,871	39,666	3,501	4,504
TOTAL (U.S.)	2,081,943	5,676,325	1,597,567	253,478	807,070

[a] Corn equivalent.
[b] Barley equivalent.
[c] Wet tons.
[d] Soybean oilmeal equivalent.

TABLE A7 Annual Crop and Livestock Production: Hay-Pasture and Livestock Feeding, as in Table A6. Year 2000 Projection Model F (Fragile Lands in 18 River Basins Unused)

River Basins	All Hay and Pasture[a]	Livestock (1,000 head)			
		Dairy Cows	Beef Cows	Beef Feeding	Hogs[b]
New England	436	0	0	0	0
Middle Atlantic	4,227	0	334	423	0
South Atlantic-Gulf	26,557	1,578	382	633	2,547
Great Lakes	31,111	3,619	384	0	4,090
Ohio	28,514	802	4,624	1,164	42,273
Tennessee	6,350	0	5,329	0	0
Upper Mississippi	68,893	0	4,183	0	48,452
Lower Mississippi	15,211	0	2,983	0	0
Souris-Red-Rainy	8,442	0	11,531	0	0
Missouri	149,196	0	23,412	6,039	38,257
Arkansas-White-Red	74,036	0	11,502	18,537	0
Texas-Gulf	48,119	307	1,923	22,500	0
Rio Grande	11,868	595	5,470	3,907	0
Upper Colorado	5,110	0	1,995	1,188	0
Lower Colorado	6,633	1,130	0	501	0
Great Basin	5,340	0	0	0	0
Columbia-North Pacific	23,848	0	2,012	1,817	0
California-South Pacific	26,393	14	3,714	2,756	0
TOTAL (United States)	540,284	8,045	79,778	59,465	135,619

[a] In 1,000 tons hay equivalent.
[b] Assumes 220 lb/head live weight.

TABLE A8 Livestock Feed Consumption: Year 2000 Projection on Model F (United States Fragile Lands Unused)

Class	Feed Grains (1,000 bushels)	Wheat (1,000 bushels)	Oilmeals[a] (1,000 cwt)	Forages[b] (1,000 tons)
Beef cows	224,378	0	756	505,132
Beef feeding	2,198,164	335,864	116,131	62,377
Dairy	669,889	12,426	90,743	43,298
Hogs	1,663,949	348,465	158,852	0
Sheep and lambs	15,163	73	8,575	8,483
Broilers	367,160	1,727	151,776	0
Turkeys	140,917	7,080	65,573	296
Eggs	314,404	19,194	64,348	531
Other	400,039	0	7,680	0
TOTAL	5,994,063	724,829	664,434	620,117

[a] Includes soybean and cottonseed.
[b] Includes tame and wild hay, silage of corn and sorghum, in hay equivalent tons.

TABLE A9   Projection of Average Price Received by United States Farmers in Year 2000 (Models A, B, and F)

		Actual	Projection for 2000 or Model		
Item	Unit	1969[a]	A[b]	B[b]	F
Crop					
Corn-sorghum[c]	$/bushel	1.12	1.11	0.94	1.05
Barley-oats[d]	$/bushel	0.88	1.03	0.90	0.97
Soybeans	$/bushel	2.33	2.25	1.78	2.10
Wheat	$/bushel	1.24	1.49	1.22	1.41
Cotton	$/bushel	0.21	0.14	0.14	0.14
Sugar beets	$/ton	f	8.62	8.16	8.40
Hay	$/ton	25.00	25.01	21.11	23.88
Silage[e]	$/ton	f	7.10	6.19	6.86
Livestock Products[g]					
Cattle and calves[h]	$/lb	0.262	0.339	0.299	0.328
Hogs[h]	$/lb	0.222	0.153	0.135	0.148
Milk	$/cwt	5.46	3.42	3.22	3.34

SOURCE: NWC Report, Table 4.52, p. IV-125.
[a] Agricultural Prices from 1969 Annual Survey, Statistical Reporting Service. PR. 1-3(70). U.S. Department of Agriculture, Washington, D.C. June, 1970.
[b] Price projections in 1970 equivalent dollars, without inflation adjustment 1970–2000.
[c] Corn equivalent.
[d] Barley equivalent.
[e] Wet tons.
[f] Not available.
[g] Assumed year 2000 prices, all models in cents: lamb, 24.5 av.; broilers, 15; eggs, 35/dozen.
[h] Live weight.

References

Acree, F., Jr., M. Beroza and M. C. Bowman. 1963. Codistillation of DDT with water. J. Agric. Food Chem. 11:278–280.

Adams, J. B. 1960. Effective spraying of 2,4-D amine on coccinellid larvae. Can. J. Zool. 38:285–288.

Adams, J. B., and M. E. Drew. 1965. Grain aphids in New Brunswick. III. Aphid populations in herbicide treated oat fields. Can. J. Zool. 43:789–794.

Advisory Commission on Intergovernmental Relations. 1968. Urban and Rural America: Policies for Future Growth. U.S. Government Printing Office, Washington, D.C.

Akesson, N. B., W. E. Yates and R. W. Brazelton. 1971a. Spray Atomization, Application Volume, Coverage and Drift. Personal communication.

Akesson, N. B., S. E. Wilce and W. E. Yates. 1971b. Confining Aerial Applications to Treated Fields—A Realistic Goal. Agrichem. Age 14(12):11–14.

Aldrich, S. R., W. R. Oschwald and J. B. Fehrenbacher. 1970. Implications of Crop Production Technology for Environmental Quality. Presented at the 137th Annual Meeting of the AAAS, Chicago, Ill.

Allison, F. E. 1966. The Fate of Nitrogen in Soils. Advan. Agron. 18:219–258.

Allred, E. R. 1966. Farm-Waste Management Trends in Northern Europe. In *Management of Farm Animal Wastes.* ASAE Publication No. SP-0366. American Society of Agricultural Engineers, St. Joseph, Mich.

American Chemical Society. 1969. Pesticides in the Environment. In *Cleaning our Environment: The Chemical Basis for Action.* American Chemical Society, Washington, D.C. pp. 195–244.

American Institute of Architects. 1971a. Establishment of a National Land Use Policy. Testimony given to the Subcommittee on Environment, Committee on

169

Interior and Insular Affairs, U.S. House of Representatives, Washington, D.C., at hearing on Nov. 8, 1971. American Institute of Architects, Washington, D.C.

American Institute of Architects. 1971b. Report of the National Policy Task Force. American Institute of Architects, Washington, D.C.

American Society of Agricultural Engineers. 1966. *Management of Farm Animal Wastes*. Proceedings of the National Symposium on Animal Waste Management. ASAE Publ. No. SP-0366. American Society of Agricultural Engineers, St. Joseph, Mich.

American Society of Agricultural Engineers. 1971. *Livestock Waste Management and Pollution Abatement*. Proceedings of the International Symposium on Livestock Wastes. ASAE Publ. PROC-271. American Society of Agricultural Engineers, St. Joseph, Mich.

American Society of Civil Engineers. Hydraulics Division. Committee on Sedimentation. 1962. Sediment Transportation Mechanics: Erosion of Sediment. Progress Report by the Task Committee on Preparation of Sediment Manual. Journal of the Hydraulics Division 88 (No. HY4).

Anderson, G. R., and C. O. Baker. 1950. Some Effects of 2,4-D in representative Idaho soils. Agron. J. 42:456–458.

Anderson, J. M., and M. R. Peterson. 1969. DDT: Sublethal effects on brook trout nervous system. Science 162:440–441.

Anon. 1968. A National Program of Research for Environmental Quality–Pollution in Relation to Agriculture and Forestry. Join Task Force of USDA and the State Universities and Land Grant Colleges, Washington, D.C.

Anon. 1969. *Animal Waste Management*. Cornell Conference on Agricultural Waste Management. Syracuse, N.Y.

Anon. 1972. *Results of Waste Management Research*. Proceedings of the Conference on Agricultural Waste Management. Cornell University, Ithaca, N.Y.

Association of State Universities and Land Grant Colleges and U.S. Department of Agriculture. 1966. A National Program of Research for Agriculture. U.S. Department of Agriculture, Washington, D.C.

Avigan, J., and M. Blumer. 1968. On the origin of pristane in marine organisms. J. Lipid Res. 9:350–352.

Bartlett, H. D., and L. F. Marriott. 1971. Subsurface Disposal of Liquid Manure. In *Livestock Waste Management and Pollution Abatement*. Proceedings of the International Symposium on Livestock Wastes. ASAE Publ. PROC-271, pp. 258–260. American Society of Agricultural Engineers, St. Joseph, Mich.

Bell, R. G., and J. Pos. 1970. The Design and Operation of a Pilot Plant for Composting Poultry Manure. ASAE paper No. 70–419, presented Annual Meeting, Minneapolis, Minn.

Bennett, I., and O. F. Freeman. 1969. Control of Agriculture-Related Pollution. A Report to the President submitted by Office of Science and Technology and the Secretary of Agriculture.

Bennett, S. E., L. M. Josephson and E. E. Burgess. 1967. Field and laboratory studies of resistance of corn to the corn earworm. J. Econ. Entomol. 60:171–173.

Berry, J. H. 1971. A Comparison of Projections of Fertilizer Use by 1980. Fertilizer Situation. USDA Economics Research Service, Washington, D.C.

Biggar, J. W., and R. B. Corey. 1969. Agricultural Drainage and Eutrophication. In *Eutrophication: Causes, Consequences, Correctives*. National Academy of Sciences, Washington, D.C. pp. 404–445.

Black, C. A. 1968. *Soil–Plant Relations* (2nd Ed.). John Wiley and Sons, New York. Chapters 7, 8, 9; pp. 179–319.

Black, C. A. 1970. Behavior of Soil and Fertilizer Phosphorus in Relation to Water Pollution. In *Agricultural Practices and Water Quality*. Iowa State University Press, Ames. pp. 72–93.

Blumer, M. 1967. Hydrocarbons in digestive tract and liver of a basking shark. Science 156:390–391.

Bormann, F. H., G. E. Likens, D. W. Fisher and R. S. Pierce. 1968. Nutrient Loss Accelerated by Clearcutting of a Forest Ecosystem. Science 159:882–884.

Borsody, L. 1966. Beef and veal production in Western Europe—trends and prospects. Monthly Bull. Agric. & Econ. Status 15(12):9–18.

Bower, C. A., and L. V. Wilcox. 1969. Nitrate Content of the Upper Rio Grande as Influenced by Nitrogen Fertilization of Adjacent Irrigated Lands. Soil Sci. Soc. Amer. Proc. 33:971–973.

Bowman, M. C., F. Acree, Jr., and M. K. Crobett. 1960. Solubility of carbon-14 DDT in water. J. Agric. Food Chem. 8:406–408.

Boyd, C. E. 1964. Insecticides cause mosquito fish to abort. Progr. Fish-Cult. 26:138.

Bracey, H. E. 1971. Conservation and Rural Development in Great Britain. Sci. Rev. 9(2):1–48.

Braids, O. C. 1972. Land Disposal Management of Livestock Wastes. In *Proceedings of Livestock Waste Management Conference*. Department of Agricultural Engineering, University of Illinois, Urbana. 21 pp.

Bridges, W. R., and A. K. Andrews. 1961. Effects of DDT spray on fish and aquatic insects in Gallatin River drainage in Montana. U.S. Fish Wildl. Serv. Spec. Sci. Report: Fisheries No. 391. 4 p.

Brown, A. W. A. 1969. Insecticide resistance and the future control of insects. Can. Med. Assoc. J. 100:216–221.

Brown, L. R. 1963. Man, Land and Food. Foreign Agric. Econ. Rept. No. 11. USDA Economic Research Service, Washington, D.C.

Burdick, G. E., E. J. Harris, H. J. Dean, T. M. Walker, J. Skea and D. Colby. 1964. The accumulation of DDT in lake trout and the effect on reproduction. Trans. Amer. Fish Soc. 93:127–136.

Bureau of Governmental Research and Service—University of Oregon. 1970. Map/ Model System. System Description and User's Guide, University of Oregon, Eugene.

Burnett, W. E., and N. C. Dondero. 1968. The Control of Air Pollution (Odors) from Animal Wastes—Evaluation of Commercial Odor Control Products by an Organoleptic Test. ASAE paper No. 68–609. Presented at the Winter Meeting, American Society of Agricultural Engineers, Chicago, Ill.

Burnett, W. E., and N. C. Dondero. 1969. Microbiological and Chemical Changes in Poultry Manure Associated with Decomposition and Odor Generation. Proceedings of the Conference on Agricultural Waste Management, p. 271. Cornell University, Ithaca, N.Y.

Burnett, W. E., and A. T. Sobel. 1968. Odors, Gases, and Particulate Matter from High Density Poultry Management Systems as They Relate to Air Pollution. Proj. Rept. No. 2, N.Y. State Contract 1101, Oct. 1967–April 1968. Cornell University, Ithaca, N.Y.

Butler, P. A. 1964. Commercial fisheries investigations. In *The Effects of Pesticides on Fish and Wildlife*. U.S. Fish Wildl. Serv. Circ. 226. pp. 65–77.

Butler, P. A. 1969. The sub-lethal effects of pesticide pollution. In *The Biological Impact of Pesticides in the Environment*. Environmental Health Series No. 1, pp. 87–89. Oregon State University, Corvallis.

Cahn, R., R. Phipers and E. Brodaty. 1945. Stability of derris in insecticidal dusts. The solvent–powder effect. J. Soc. Chem. Ind. (London) 64:33.

Chakrabarty, A. M., and I. C. Gunsalus. 1970. Transduction and genetic homology between *Pseudomonas* species *putida* and *aeruginosa*. J. Bact. 103:830–832.

Chakrabarty, A. M., and I. C. Gunsalus. 1971. CAM plasmid in pseudomonads: transfer polarity and genetic circularity. Bact. Proc. G 137.

Chemical Week. 1963. Pesticides. Chemical Week Report, May 25, 1963.

Chen, Y. L., and J. E. Casida. 1969. Photodecomposition of pyrethrin 1, allethrin, phalthrin and dimethrin. Modifications in the acid moiety. J. Agric. Food Chem. 17:208–215.

Chutney, L. 1970. W,ashington Report—Council on Environmental Quality. Design and Environment 1(3):6–7.

Cicchetti, C. J. 1971. Some Economic Issues in Planning Urban Recreation Facilities. In *Land Economics*. University of Wisconsin Press, Madison. 47:15–23.

Clarke, D. D., W. J. Niklas and J. Palumbo. 1968. Fluoromalate: a substrate for fumarate hydratase. Arch. Biochem. Biophys. 123:205–216.

Clawson, M. 1959. Methods of Measuring the Demand for and Value of Outdoor Recreation. Rept. No. 10. Resources for the Future, Inc., Washington, D.C.

Clawson, M., R. B. Held and C. Stoddard. 1960. *Land for the Future*. The Johns Hopkins Press, Baltimore, Md.

Clawson, M., and J. L. Knetsch. 1966. Economics of Outdoor Recreation. Resources for the Future, Inc., Washington, D.C.

Cochran, C. L. 1971. The Scandal of Rural Housing. The Architectural Forum 134(2):52–55.

Cole, H., D. MacKenzie, C. B. Smith and E. L. Bergman. 1968. Influence of various persistent chlorinated insecticides on the macro and micro element constituents of *Zea mays* and *Phaseolus vulgaris* growing in soil containing various amounts of these materials. Bull. Environ. Contam. Toxicol. 3:141–154.

Converse, J. C., D. L. Day, J. T. Pfeffer and B. A. Jones. 1971. Aeration with ORP Control to Suppress Odors Emitted from Liquid Swine Manure Systems. In *Livestock Waste Management and Pollution Abatement*. Proceedings of the International Symposium on Livestock Wastes. ASAE Publ. PROC-271, pp. 267–271. American Society of Agricultural Engineers, St. Joseph, Mich.

Cooper, C. F. 1969. Nutrient Output from Managed Forests. In *Eutrophication: Causes, Consequences, Correctives*. National Academy of Sciences, Washington, D.C. pp. 446–463.

Corneliussen, P. E. 1970. Pesticide Residues in Total Diet Samples. V. Pesticide Monitoring Journal 4(3):89–105.

Council on Environmental Quality. 1970. First Annual Report. U.S. Government Printing Office, Washington, D.C.

Council on Environmental Quality. 1971. Second Annual Report. U.S. Government Printing Office, Washington, D.C.

Crosby, D. G. 1969. Symposium on natural food toxicants: coordinator's introduction. J. Agric. Food Chem. 17:413.

Crosby, D. G. 1971. Environmental Photooxidation of Pesticides. In *Degradation of Synthetic Organic Molecules in the Biosphere*, pp. 260–278. National Academy of Sciences, Washington, D.C. (ISBN 0-309-02046-8).

Dagley, S. 1971. Catabolism of aromatic compounds by microorganisms. Advan. Microbial Physiol. 6:1–46.

Decker, W. M., and J. H. Steele. 1966. Health Aspects and Vector Control Associated with Animal Wastes. Proceedings of the National Symposium on Animal Waste Management, ASAE Publ. No. SP-0366, p. 18. American Society of Agricultural Engineers, St. Joseph, Mich.

Deibel, R. H. 1967. Biological Aspects of the Animal Waste Disposal Problem, in *Agriculture and the Quality of Our Environment,* AAAS Publ. No. 85, 395.

Deichmann, W. B., and W. E. MacDonald. 1971. Organochlorine Pesticides and Human Health. Fed. Cosmet. Toxicol. 9:91–103.

Dickey, E., W. D. Lembke, T. R. Peck, G. Stone and W. H. Walker. 1972. Nitrate Levels and Possible Sources in Shallow Wells. *Environmental Quality and Agriculture. What are the Options?* Special Publ. 26, College of Agriculture, University of Illinois, Urbana. pp. 40–43.

Dickey, J. W. 1969. Mass Transit Exchange Bibliography Nos. 98 and 99. Committee of Planning Librarians, Monticello, Ill.

Diesch, S. L., B. S. Pomeroy and E. R. Allred. 1971. Survival and Detection of Leptrospires in Aerated Beef Cattle Manure. In *Livestock Waste Management and Pollution Abatement.* Proceedings of the International Symposium on Livestock Wastes. ASAE Publ. PROC-271, pp. 263–266. American Society of Agricultural Engineers, St. Joseph, Mich.

Duggan, R. E. and J. R. Weatherwax. 1967. Dietary intake of pesticide chemicals. Science 157(3792):1006–1010.

Duggan, R. E. and G. Q. Lipscomb. 1969. Dietary intake of pesticide chemicals in the United States. II. June 1966–April 1968. Pesticide Mont. J. 2:153.

Durost, D. D. 1971. The Outlook for 1980—Cropland Acres, *Fertilizer Situation.* USDA Economic Research Service, Washington, D.C. (March).

Environmental Awareness Center. 1971. *Madison E-Way System.* University of Wisconsin, Madison.

Evans, W. C., B. S. W. Smith, P. Moss and H. N. Fernley. 1971. Bacterial metabolism of 4-chlorophenoxyacetate. Biochem. J. 122:509–517.

Faith, W. L. 1964. Odor Control in Cattle Feed Yards. J. Air Poll. Cont. Assn. 14:459.

FAO/WHO. 1967. Pesticide Residues in Food. WHO Tech. Rept. Ser. No. 370. World Health Organization, Geneva.

FDA. 1970. Product Safety Report: Poison Control—Ingestion Reports Submitted to the Poison Control Division, January–June 1969. FDA Papers 4(4):29–31.

Felch, R. E., and G. L. Barger. 1971. EPIMAY and Southern corn leaf blight. Weekly Weather and Crop Bulletin 58 (43):13–17.

Ferguson, D. E., W. D. Cotton, D. T. Gardner and D. D. Culley. 1965. Tolerances to five chlorinated hydrocarbon insecticides in two species of fish from a transect of the lower Mississippi River. J. Mississippi Acad. Sci. 11:239–245.

Flint, C. L. 1873. Massachusetts State Board of Agriculture. 21st Annual Report. Massachusetts State Board of Agriculture, State House, Boston.

Focht. D. D., and M. Alexander. 1970. DDT metabolites and analogs:ring fission by *Hydrogenomonas.* Science 170:91–92.

Frawley, J. P., J. W. Cook, J. R. Blake and O. G. Fitzhugh. 1958. Effect of light on chemical and biological properties of parathion. J. Agric. Food Chem. 6:28–30.

Freeman, O. F., and I. L. Bennett, Jr. 1969. *Control of Agriculture-Related Pollution.* A Report to the President. Office of Science and Technology and USDA. 102 p.

Frink, C. R. 1969. Water Pollution Potential Estimated from Farm Nutrient Budgets. Agron. J. 61:550–553.

Frink, C. R. 1971. Plant Nutrients and Water Quality. Agricultural Science Review (second quarter) 9(2):11–25.

Fuguitt, G. V. 1971. The Places Left Behind: Population Trends and Policy for Rural America. Rural Sociology, Vol. 36. Dec.

Fuller, B. 1969. *Operating Manual for Spaceship Earth.* Southern Illinois University Press, Carbondale. 143 pp.

FWPCA. 1968. Water Quality Control and Management in Snake River Basin. Federal Water Pollution Control Administration, Portland, Ore.

Fyfe, R. W., J. Campbell, B. Hayson and K. Hodson. 1969. Regional population declines in organochlorine insecticides in Canadian prairie falcons. Can. Field Nat. 83:191–200.

Gaffney, M. 1964. Containment Policies for Urban Sprawl. University of Kansas Publications. Government Research Series No. 27, Lawrence, Kan.

Gamar, Y. and J. K. Gaunt. 1971. Bacterial metabolism of 4-chloro-2-methylphenoxyacetate. Biochem. J. 122:527–531.

Garman, W. H. 1970. Agricultural Nutrient Budget. In *Nutrient Mobility in Soils: Accumulation and Losses.* Soil Science Society of America, Madison, Wisc. pp. 61–72.

Gaunt, J. K., and W. C. Evans. 1971. Metabolism of 4-chloro-2-methylphenoxyacetate by a soil pseudomonad. Biochem. J. 122:533–542.

Gilbertson, C. B. 1970. Design Considerations for Control of Beef Feedlot Waste. Paper presented at Midwestern Animal Waste Management Conference, National Livestock Feeders Association, Omaha, Neb.

Goldberg, E. O., P. Butler, P. Meier, D. Menzel, G. Paulik, R. Risebrough and L. F. Stikel. 1971. Chlorinated hydrocarbons in the marine environment. National Academy of Sciences, Washington, D.C.

Goldberg, M. C. 1970. Sources of Nitrogen in Water Supplies. In *Agricultural Practices and Water Quality.* Iowa State University Press, Ames. pp. 94–124.

Goldstein, J. H. 1971. Competition for Wetlands in the Midwest. An Economic Analysis. Resources for the Future, Inc., Washington, D.C.

Gumerman, R. C., and D. A. Carlson. 1969. Hydrogen Sulfide and Methyl Mercaptan Removals with Soil Columns. Proceedings 21st Industrial Waste Conference. Purdue University, Lafayette, Ind.

Guy, G. P. 1963. Residential Construction and Sedimentation at Kensington, Maryland. Paper No. 3. Proceedings of the Federal Inter-Agency Sedimentation Conference. Misc. Publ. No. 970, pp. 30–37. USDA Agricultural Research Service, Washington, D.C.

Hall–Kane Associates and Landscapes, Inc. 1970. Indiana Dunes National Lakeshore Prototype Study, Phase I. Hall–Kane Assoc., Gary, Ind., and Landscapes, Inc., Madison, Wisc.

Hammond, A. L. 1971. Weather Modification: A Technology Coming of Age. Science 172:548.

Hammond, W. C., D. L. Day and E. L. Hansen. 1968. Can Lime and Chlorine Suppress Odors in Liquid Hog Manure? Agric. Eng. 49:340.

Hansen, A. A. 1972. A Directed Ecosystem Approach to Pest Control and Environmental Quality. J. Environ. Quality 1:45–54.

Hansen, D. J. 1969. Behavior of estuarine organisms. In *Quarterly Report,* July 1969–September 1969. Atlantic Estuarine Fisheries Center, Beaufort, N.C.

Harrison, H. L., O. L. Loucks, J. W. Mitchell, D. F. Parkhurst, C. R. Tracy, D. G. Watts, and V. J. Yannacone, Jr. 1970. Systems studies of DDT transport. Science 170:503-508.

Hauser, P. M. 1964. Man and more men: the population prospects. Bull. of Atomic Scientists 20(6):4–8.

Hayaishi, O. 1966. Crystalline oxygenases of pseudomonads. Bact. Rev. 30:720–731.

Hayaishi, O. 1969. Enzymic hydroxylation. Ann. Rev. Biochem. 38:21–39.

Headley, J. C. 1971. Productivity of Agricultural Pesticides. In *Economic Research for Policy Decisionmaking*, Proceedings of Symposium, pp. 80–88. USDA Economic Research Service, Washington, D.C. 172 p.

Heady, E. O., E. O. Haroldsen, L. V. Mayer and L. G. Tweeten. 1965. *Roots of the Farm Problem*. Iowa State University Press, Ames.

Heady, E. O., H. C. Madsen, K. J. Nicol, S. H. Hargrove. 1972. Agricultural and Water Policies and the Environment. CARD Rept. No. 40T. Center for Agricultural and Rural Development, Iowa State University, Ames.

Heald, W. R., and R. C. Loehr. 1971. Utilization of Agricultural Wastes. USDA Yearbook of Agriculture. U.S. Government Printing Office, Washington, D.C.

Heath, R. G., J. W. Spann and J. F. Kreitzer. 1969. Marked DDE impairment of mallard reproduction in controlled studies. Nature 224:47–48.

Helgeson, E. A. 1947. The effect of 2,4-D on wheat. Proceedings of the North Central Weed Control Conference 4:37–38. State Weed Supervisor, State House, Topeka, Kan.

Helle, W. 1965. Resistance in the Acarina: mites. Advan. Acarol. 2:71–93.

Henry, J. H. 1971. A Comparison of Projections of Fertilizer Use by 1980. Fertilizer Situation. USDA Economic Research Service, Washington, D.C.

Hensler, R. F., R. J. Olsen, S. A. Witzel, O. J. Attoe, W. H. Paulson and R. F. Johannes. 1969. Effect of Method of Manure Handling on Crop Yields, Nutrient Recovery and Runoff losses. Departments of Soils and Agricultural Engineering, University of Wisconsin, Madison.

Hickey, J. J., and D. W. Anderson. 1968. Chlorinated hydrocarbons and eggshell changes in raptorial and fish-eating birds. Science 162:271–273.

Hildreth, R. J., and M. S. Williams. 1968. Fertilizer Use Economics. Chapter 17 in *Changing Patterns in Fertilizer Use*. Special Publication. Soil Science Society of America, Madison, Wisc.

Hindin, E., D. S. May, and G. H. Dunstan. 1966. Distribution of insecticides sprayed by airplane on an irrigated corn plot. In *Organic Pesticides in the Environment*. American Chemical Society, Washington, D.C. pp. 132–145.

Hoffman, C. H., H. K. Townes, R. I. Sailer and H. H. Swift. 1946. Field studies on the effects of DDT on aquatic insects. U.S. Bureau of Entomology and Plant Quarantine. Publ. E-702. United States Department of Agriculture, Washington, D.C. 20 p.

Hooper, B. 1970. The Real Change Has Just Begun. Life 68:1 (9 January, 1970).

Howes, J. R. 1966. On-site Composting of Poultry Manure. Proceedings of the National Symposium on Animal Waste Management, ASAE Publ. No. SP-0366, pp. 66–68. American Society of Agricultural Engineers, St. Joseph, Mich.

Hyslop, J. A. 1938. Losses occasioned by insects, mites, and ticks in the U.S. Bureau of Entomology and Plant Quarantine, Div. of Insect Pest Survey and Information Publ. E-444. United States Department of Agriculture, Washington, D.C. 57 pp.

Ibach, D. B., and J. N. Mahon. 1968. Fertilizer Use Patterns and Potentials. Chapter 1 in *Changing Patterns in Fertilizer Use*. Special Publication. Soil Science Society of America, Madison, Wisc.

Ide, F. P. 1957. Effects of forest spraying with DDT on aquatic insects of salmon streams. Trans. Am. Fisheries Soc. 86:208–219.

Ishii, S., and C. Hirano. 1963. Growth responses of larvae of the ricestem borer to rice plants treated with 2,4-D. Entomol. Exp. Appl. 6:257–262.

Jackson, J. B. 1965. Jefferson, Thoreau and After. Landscape 15(2):25–27.

176   *References*

Jackson, J. B. 1966. An Engineered Environment. Landscape 16(1):16–20.
Jackson, J. B. 1967. To Pity the Plumage and Forget the Dying Bird. Landscape 17(1):1–4.
James, I. C., Jr., B. T. Bower and N. C. Matalas. 1969. Relative Importance of Variables in Water Resource Planning. Resources for the Future, Inc. Water Resources Research 5:1165–1173.
Jaworski, N. A., and L. J. Hetling. 1970. Relative Contributions of Nutrients to the Potomac River Basin from Various Sources. In *Relationship of Agriculture to Soil and Water Pollution*. Proceedings of the Cornell University Conference on Agricultural Waste Management, Ithaca, N.Y. pp. 134–146.
Jedele, D. G., and F. W. Andrew. 1972. Slotted-Floor Cold-Confinement Beef-Cattle Housing. ASAE 72–448. American Society of Agricultural Engineers, St. Joseph, Mich.
Johnson, B. T., C. R. Saunders, H. Saunders and R. S. Campbell. 1971. Biological magnification and Degradation of DDT and Aldrin by Freshwater Invertebrates. J. Fish. Res. Bd. Canada 28:705–709.
Jones, D. D., D. L. Day and A. C. Dale. 1970. Aerobic Treatment of Livestock Wastes. Illinois Agr. Exp. Sta. Bull. No. 737. 55 pp.
Jones, H. A., and H. L. Haller. 1931. The "yellow compounds" resulting from the decomposition of rotenone in solution. J. Amer. Chem. Soc. 53:2320–2324.
Josephson, H. R. 1970. Private communication to Paul E. Waggoner.
Kahn, H., and A. J. Weiner. 1968. The Year 2000: A Framework for Speculation on the Next Thirty-three Years. Macmillan, New York.
Kapoor, I. P., R. L. Metcalf, A. S. Hirwe, P. Y. Lu, J. R. Coats and R. P. Nystrom. 1971. Comparative metabolism of DDT, methychlor and ethoxychlor in mouse, insects, and in a model ecosystem. J. Agric. Food Chem. 20:1–6.
Kapoor, I. P., R. L. Metcalf, R. S. Nystrom and G. K. Sangha. 1970. Comparative metabolism of methoxychlor, methiochlor, and DDT in mouse, insects, and in a model ecosystem. J. Agric. Food Chem. 18:1145–1152.
Kearney, P. C., J. R. Plimmer and P. A. Frank. 1970. Water Pollutants and Their Effects on Agriculture. Presented at the 19th Annual Meeting of the Agricultural Research Institute, Arlington, Va.
Keith, J. A. 1966. Reproduction in a population of herring gulls *Larus argentatus* contaminated by DDT. J. Appl. Ecol. 3 (Supplement of Pesticides in the Environment and Their Effects on Wildlife): 57–70.
Keith, J. O., R. M. Hansen and A. L. Ward. 1959. Effect of 2,4-D on abundance and foods of pocket gophers. J. Wildl. Manag. 23:137–145.
Keith, J. O., L. A. Woods and E. C. Hunt. 1970. Reproductive failure in brown pelicans on the Pacific coast. Transactions of the 35th North American Wildlife and Natural Resources Conference, pp. 56–63. Wildlife Management Institute, Washington, D.C.
Kemper, W. D. 1970. Technology for Reducing Soil Pollutants and Their Effects, Presented at the 19th Annual Meeting of the Agricultural Research Institute, Washington, D.C.
Kilgore, W. W., N. Marei and W. Winterlin. 1972. Parathion in Plant Tissues: New Considerations. In *Degradation of Synthetic Organic Molecules in the Biosphere*, pp. 291–312 National Academy of Sciences, Washington, D.C. (ISBN 0-309-02046-8).
Kilmer, V. J. 1967. The Role of Fertilizers in Soil and Water Conservation. In Proceedings of the 22nd Annual Meeting of the Soil Conservation Society of America, Des Moines, Iowa.

Kitchen, J. W., and J. M. James. 1968. An Analysis of Consumers Expenditures on Recreation. Research Report No. 4. Texas Tech University, College of Agricultural Sciences. Department of Park Administration, Lubbock, Tex.

Kneese, V. 1970. Protecting Our Environment and Natural Resources in the 1970's. Resources for the Future, Inc., Washington, D.C.

Knipling, E. F. 1972. Use of Organisms to Control Insect Pests. J. Environ. Quality 1:34–40.

Knowles, R. 1969. Owens Valley Study. University of Southern California, Department of Architecture, Los Angeles.

Korschgen, L. J. and D. A. Murphy. 1969. Pesticide–wildlife relationships: Reproduction, growth, and physiology of deer fed dieldrin contaminated diets. Missouri Federal Aid Project No. 13-R-21. Work Plan No. 8, Job No. 1, Progress Report. 55 p.

Krause, O. E. 1971. *Population and Land Use Trends and Projections.* USDA Economic Research Service, Washington, D.C.

Krutilla, J. V. and J. L. Knetsch. 1970. Outdoor Recreation Economics. Annals of the American Academy of Political and Social Science 389:63–70.

Landsberg, H. H. 1964. Natural Resources for U.S. Growth—A Look Ahead to the Year 2000. The Johns Hopkins Press, Baltimore, Md.

Landsberg, H. H., L. L. Fischman and J. L. Fisher. 1963. Resources in America's Future, Patterns of Requirements and Availabilities 1960–2000. The Johns Hopkins Press for Resources for the Future, Inc., Baltimore, Md.

Larson, R. E. and J. A. Moore. 1971. Beef Wastes and the Oxidation Ditch Today and Tomorrow. In *Livestock Waste Management and Pollution Abatement.* Proceedings of the International Symposium on Livestock Wastes. ASAE Publ. PROC-271, American Society of Agricultural Engineers, St. Joseph, Mich. pp. 217–219.

Lathwell, D. L., D. R. Bouldin and W. S. Reed. 1970. Effect of Nitrogen Fertilizer Applications in Agriculture. In *Relationship of Agriculture to Soil and Water Pollution.* Proceedings of the Cornell University Conference on Agricultural Waste Management, Ithaca, N.Y. pp. 192–206.

Lewis, P. H., Jr. 1969. *Regional Design for Human Impact.* Thomas Printing and Publishing Co., Kaukauna, Wisc. 317 pp.

Lichtenstein, E. P. 1972. Environmental factors affecting fate of pesticides. In *Degradation of Synthetic Organic Molecules in the Biosphere,* pp. 190–205. National Academic of Sciences, Washington, D.C. (ISBN 0-309-02046-8).

Livshutz, A. 1964. Aerobic Digestion (Composting) of Poultry Manure. World's Poultry Sci. J. 20:212–215.

Loehr, R. C. 1968. Pollution Implications of Animal Wastes: A Forward Oriented Review. USDI, Federal Water Pollution Control Administration, Wasington, D.C. 175 pp.

Loehr, R. C. 1969. Animal Wastes—A National Problem. J. San. Engr. Div., Proc. Amer. Soc. Civil Engr. 95 (SA 2):189.

Loehr, R. C. 1970. Changing Practices in Agriculture and Their Effect on the Environment. In *Critical Reviews in Environmental Control.* Chemical Rubber Co., Cleveland, Ohio.

Loehr, R. C. 1971. Alternatives for the Treatment and Disposal of Animal Wastes. J. Water Pollution Control Federation 43:668-678.

Loehr, R. C. 1972. Animal Waste Management—Problems and Guidelines for Solutions. J. Environ. Quality 1:71–78.

Loehr, R. C., D. F. Anderson and A. C. Anthonisen. 1971. An Oxidation Ditch for the Handling and Treatment of Poultry Wastes. In *Livestock Management and Pollution Abatement*. Proceedings of the International Symposium on Livestock Wastes. ASAE Publ. PROC-271, pp. 209–212. American Society of Agricultural Engineers, St. Joseph, Mich.

Lord, F. T. 1956. The influence of spray programs on the fauna of apple orchards in Nova Scotia. IX. Studies on mean of altering predator populations. Can. Entomol. 88:129–137.

Madden, J. M. and J. N. Dornbush. 1971. Measurement of Runoff and Runoff Carried Waste from Commercial Feedlots. In *Livestock Waste Management and Pollution Abatement*. Proceedings of the International Symposium on Livestock Wastes. ASAE Publ. PROC-271, pp. 44–47. American Society of Agricultural Engineers, St. Joseph, Mich.

Mannering, J. V., and R. E. Burwell. 1968. Tillage Methods to Reduce Runoff and Erosion in the Corn Belt. U.S. Department of Agriculture Inf. Bull. No. 330. U.S. Government Printing Office, Washington, D.C.

Marlatt, C. L. 1904. The annual loss occasioned by destructive insects in the United States. USDA Yearbook, pp. 461–474. U.S. Government Printing Office, Washington, D.C.

Martin, W. P., W. E. Fenster and L. D. Hansen. 1970. Fertilizer Management for Pollution Control. In *Agricultural Practices and Water Quality*, T. L. Willrich and G. E. Smith (eds.). Iowa State University Press, Ames. pp. 142–158.

Maxwell, R. C., and R. F. Harwood. 1960. Increased reproduction of pea aphids on broad beans treated with 2,4-D. Ann. Entomol. Soc. Am. 53:199–205.

McAllister, J. S. V. 1971. Nutrient Balance on Livestock Farms. Potassium and Systems of Grassland Farming. 1st Colloquium of the Potassium Institute, Ltd., Belfast, N. Ireland.

McCalla, T. M., and L. F. Elliott, 1971. The Role of Microorganisms in the Management of Animal Wastes on Beef Cattle Feedlots. In *Livestock Waste Management and Pollution Abatement*. Proceedings of the International Symposium on Livestock Wastes, ASAE Publ. PROC-271, pp. 132–134. American Society of Agricultural Engineers, St. Joseph, Mich.

McCormack, R. J. 1971. The Canada Land Use Inventory: A Basis for Land Use Planning. J. of Soil and Water Conservation. pp. 141–145.

McCoy, E. 1969. Removal of Pollution Bacteria from Animal Waste by Soil Percolation. Presented at the Annual Meeting, American Society Agricultural Engineers, Lafayette, Ind.

McHarg, I. 1969. Design with Nature. Natural History Press, Garden City, N.Y.

McKenna, E. J. and R. E. Kallio. 1964. Hydrocarbon structure: its effect on bacterial utilization of alkanes. In *Principles and Applications in Aquatic Microbiology*, H. Heukelekian and N. C. Dondero (eds.). John Wiley and Sons, New York. pp. 1–14.

McKenna, E. J., and R. E. Kallio. 1971. Microbial metabolism of the isoprenoid alkane pristane. Proc. Nat. Acad. Sci. (USA) 68:1552–1554.

Metcalf, C. L., W. P. Flint and R. L. Metcalf. 1962. *Destructive and useful insects.* McGraw-Hill, New York. 1087 pp.

Metcalf, R. L. 1971. Putting pesticides and pollution in perspective. Summaries of presentations to the 23rd Illinois Custom Spray Operators Training School. University of Illinois Extension Service, Urbana.

Metcalf, R. L., G. K. Sangha and I. P. Kapoor. 1971. Model ecosystems for the evaluation of pesticide biodegradability and ecological magnification. Environ. Sci. Technol. 5:709–713.

Metropolitan Planning Commission. 1967. Maps and Computers. Locational Information Processing for Planning and Government, Portland, Ore.

Meyer, L. D. and J. V. Mannering. 1967. Tillage and Land Modification for Water Erosion Control. Tillage for Greater Crop Production. Conference Proceedings (December 11 and 12), ASAE Publ. PROC-168, pp. 58–62. American Society of Agricultural Engineers, St. Joseph, Mich.

Meyers, C. R., Jr. 1971. New Tools for Regional Planning. AIA Journal (Oct. 37–40).

Miller, W. E. and J. C. Tash. 1967. Interim Report Upper Klamath Lake Studies Oregon. FWPCA Publ. WP-20-8. Federal Water Pollution Control Administration, Washington, D.C. p. 37.

Miner, J. R. (ed.) 1971. Farm Animal–Waste Management. (North Central Regional Research Publication 206) Iowa Agricultural Experimental Station Spec. Rep. 67. 44 pp.

Miner, J. R., R. I. Lipper, L. R. Fina and J. W. Funk. 1966. Cattle Feedlot Runoff—Its Nature and Variation. J. Water Pollut. Contr. Fed. 38:1582.

Miner, J. R. and T. L. Willrich, 1970. Livestock Operations and Field-Spread Manure as Sources of Pollutants. In *Agricultural Practices and Water Quality*, T. L. Willrich and G. E. Smith (eds.). Iowa State University Press, Ames. pp. 231–240.

Minshall, N. E., S. A. Witzel and M. S. Nichols. 1969. Effect of Time on Manure Application on Plant Nutrient Losses in Surface Runoff. Departments of Agricultural and Civil Eng., University of Wisconsin, Madison.

Morrison, W. E. and C. L. Readling. 1968. An Energy Model for the U.S. USDI. Bureau of Mines Info. Circ. No. 8384. U.S. Department of the Interior, Washington, D.C.

Muehling, A. J. 1967. Production-Line Confinement Swine Housing. ASAE 67-912. Department of Agricultural Engineering, University of Illinois, Urbana.

Muehling, A. J. 1969. Swine Housing and Waste Management. A Research Review. AEng-873. Department of Agricultural Engineering, University of Illinois, Urbana.

Naegele, R. E. 1971. Federal Pesticide Control Act of 1971: statement at hearings before the Committee on Agriculture, House of Representatives of the 92nd Congress, Serial No. 92-A. U.S. Government Printing Office, Washington, D.C. pp. 288–316.

Nash, R. G. and M. L. Beall, Jr. 1970. Chlorinated hydrocarbon insecticides: root uptake versus vapor contamination of soybean foliage. Science 168:1109–1111.

NAS. 1966a. Alternatives in Water Management. Report of the Committee on Water. NAS-NRC Publication 1408. National Academic of Sciences, Washington, D.C.

NAS. 1966b. Weather and Climate Modifications, Problems and Prospects. NAS-NRC Publication No. 1350. National Academy of Sciences, Washington, D.C.

NAS. 1968a. Water and Choice in the Colorado Basin. Report of the Committee on Water. NAS-NRC Publication 1689. National Academy of Sciences, Washington, D.C. 107 pp.

NAS. 1968b. *Weed Control*. Vol. 2 of the series: Principles of Plant and Animal Pest Control. NAS-NRC Publ. 1597. National Academy of Sciences, Washington, D.C. 477 pp.

NAS. 1969a. A Program for Outdoor Recreation Research. NAS Publ. 1727. National Academy of Sciences, Washington, D.C. 90 pp.

NAS. 1969b. Insect Pest Management and Control. Vol. 3 of the series: Principles of Plant and Animal Pest Control. NAS-NRC Publ. 1696. National Academy of Sciences, Washington, D.C. 508 pp.

National Advisory Committee on Food and Fiber. 1967. *Food and Fiber for the Future.* Report of the National Advisory Committee on Food and Fiber. U.S. Government Printing Office, Washington, D.C.

National Fertilizer Development Center. 1970. Fertilizer Summary Data. TVA, Muscle Shoals, Alabama.

National Science Foundation. 1971. Environmental Science—Challenge for the Seventies. Report of the National Science Board. NSF Publication No. NSB 71-1.

Nelson, L. B. 1972. Agricultural Chemicals in Relation to Environmental Quality: Chemical Fertilizers, Present and Future. J. Environ. Qual. 1:2-6.

Niemer, H., H. Bucherer and H. Kohler. 1959. Uber den Abbau von Atropin durch *Corynebacterium belladonnae,* I. Hoppe-Seylers Z. Physiol. Chem. 317:238-242.

Niemer, H. and H. Bucherer. 1961. Uber den Abbau von Atropin durch *Corynebacterium belladonnae, II.* Hoppe Seylers Z. Physiol. Chem. 326:9-12.

Northeastern Illinois Planning Commission. 1971. Regional Open Space Plan—An element of the Comprehensive General Plan for Northeastern Illinois. Northeastern Illinois Planning Commission, Chicago.

Norton, T. E., and R. W. Hansen. 1969. Cattle Feedlot Water Quality Hydrology. In Proceedings, Agricultural Waste Management Conference, Cornell University, Ithaca, N.Y.

Owens, T. R., and W. L. Griffin. 1968. Economics of Water Pollution Control for Cattle Feedlot Operations. Spec. Rept. No. 9, Department of Agricultural Economics. Texas Tech University, Lubbock.

Painter, R. H. 1951. *Insect Resistance in Crop Plants.* Macmillan Co., New York.

Palmby, C. D. 1971. Statement before Subcommittee on Foreign Economic Policy of Joint Economic Committee—U.S. Congress. In *Foreign Economic Policy for the 1970's.* (June 28, 1971). U.S. Government Printing Office, Washington, D.C.

Paradis, R. O. 1956. Factors in the recent importance of the red-banded leaf roller, *Arqyrotaenia velutinana* (Walker), in Quebec apple orchards. Quebec Soc. Protection Plants, Rept. No. 38:45-48.

Pavelis, G. A., and C. Gertel. 1963. The Management and Use of Water. USDA Yearbook of Agriculture. U.S. Government Printing Office, Washington, D.C. pp. 83-93.

Pawley, W. H. 1963. Possibilities of increasing world food production. United Nations–Food and Agricultural Organization FFHC Basic Study No. 10. Rome.

Pecora, W. T. 1971. Nature, Not Only Man, Degrades Environment. Speech given at George Washington University, Washington, D.C. USDI Geological Survey News Release.

Pesek, J., and R. A. Olsen. 1970. Workshop Session. In *Agricultural Practices and Water Quality.* Iowa State University Press, Ames.

Pneu Michelin. 1971. *1971 Michelin—France* (Red Guide). Services de Tourisme, Paris, France.

Pimentel, D. 1961. An ecological approach to the insecticide problem. J. Econ. Entomol. 54:108-114.

Pimentel, D., D. W. Hayne, L. A. Krumholz, J. T. Middleton, L. A. Walford and J. L. Buckley. 1965a. Effects of Pollutants on Living Organisms Other than Man. In *Restoring the Quality of Our Environment* (Report of the Environmental Pollution Panel, President's Science Advisory Committee), pp. 192-226. U.S. Government Printing Office, Washington, D.C.

Pimentel, D., D. Chant, A. Kelman, R. L. Metcalf, L. D. Newsom, C. Smith. 1965b. Improved Pest Control Practices. In *Restoring the Quality of Our Environment* (Report of the Environmental Pollution Panel, President's Science Advisory Committee), pp. 227–291. U.S. Government Printing Office, Washington, D.C.

Pimentel, D. 1971. Ecological effects of pesticides on non-target species. Executive Office of Science and Technology. U.S. Government Printing Office, Washington, D.C. 220 pp.

Pimentel, D. 1972. Pesticides, pollution and food supply. Report 72-1. Department of Entomology, Cornell University, Ithaca, N.Y. 38 pp.

Pimentel, D., and C. Shoemaker. 1972. Insecticide Reduction on Cotton and Corn—Economics and Land Use. Mimeo available from Department of Entomology, Cornell University, Ithaca, N.Y. 37 pp.

Porter, R. D., and S. N. Wiemeyer. 1969. Dieldrin and DDT: Effects on sparrow hawk eggshells and reproduction. Science 165:199–200.

Pos, J., R. G. Bell and J. B. Robinson. 1971. Aerobic Treatment of Liquid and Solid Poultry Manure. In *Livestock Management and Pollution Abatement.* Proceedings of the International Symposium on Livestock Wastes. ASAE Publ. PROC-21. American Society of Agricultural Engineers, St. Joseph, Mich. pp. 220–224.

Post, R. L., R. W. McCalley and J. A. Munro. 1949. Insecticidal applications and potato yields in North Dakota for 1949. N. Dak. Agr. Exp. Sta. Bimo. Bull. 12(2):42–46.

Power, J. F. 1970. Leaching of Nitrate–Nitrogen Under Dry-Land Agriculture in the Northern Great Plains. In *Relationship of Agriculture to Soil and Water Pollution.* Proceedings of the Cornell University Conference on Agricultural Waste Management, Ithaca, N.Y. pp. 111–122.

President's National Advisory Commission on Rural Poverty. 1968. Rural Poverty in the United States. U.S. Government Printing Office, Washington, D.C.

Priester, L. E. 1965. The accumulation in metabolism of DDT, parathion, and endrin by aquatic food-chain organisms. Ph.D. Thesis, Clemson University, Clemson, S.C. 74 pp.

Public Law 91-609. Title VII Housing and Urban Development Act of 1970, approved December 31, 1970, titled "Urban Growth and New Community Act of 1970." U.S. Government Printing Office, Washington, D.C.

Putnam, P. C. 1953. Energy in the Future. D. Van Nostrand Co., New York.

Rainey, R. H. 1967. Natural displacement of pollution from the Great Lakes. Science 155:1242–1243.

Rose, W. W., J. E. Chapman, S. Roseid, A. Katsuyama, V. Porter and W. A. Mercer. 1965. Composting Fruit and Vegetable Refuse. Compost Sci., pp. 13–25 (Summer).

Rosen, J. D. and D. J. Sutherland. 1967. The nature and toxicity of the photoconversion products of aldrin. Bull. Environ. Contam. Toxicol. 2:1.

Rosenberry, P. E. and W. C. Moldenhaur. 1971. Economic Implications of Conservation and Sediment Control. J. Soil and Water Conservation 26:220–224.

Ruttan, V. M. 1965. The Economic Demand for Irrigated Agriculture: New Methodology and Some Preliminary Projections, 1954–1980. The Johns Hopkins Press, Baltimore, Md.

Scheltinga, H. M. J. 1966. Biological Treatment of Animal Wastes. In *Management of Farm Animal Wastes.* ASAE Publ. No. SP-0366, American Society of Agricultural Engineers, St. Joseph, Mich.

Searl, M. F. 1960. Fossil Fuels in the Future. U.S. Atomic Energy Commission Publication No. TID8209.

Smith, G. E. 1967. Fertilizer Nutrients as Contaminants in Water Supplies. In *Agriculture and the Quality of Our Environment*. AAAS Publ. 85, pp. 173–186. Washington, D.C. 460 p.

Solnit, A. 1966. What's the Use of Small Towns? Landscape 16(1):3–6.

Sporn, P. 1963. Energy, Its Production, Conversion and Use in the Service of Man. The Macmillan Co., New York.

Stahler, L. M. and E. I. Whitehead. 1950. The effect of 2,4-D on potassium nitrate levels in leaves of sugar beets. Science 112:749–751.

Stall, J. B. 1962. Soil Conservation Can Reduce Reservoir Sedimentation. Public Works Magazine 93(9):125–128.

Stanford, G., C. B. England and A. W. Taylor. 1970. Fertilizer Use and Water Quality. USDA-ARS Publ. 41-168. U.S. Department of Agriculture, Washington, D.C.

Starks, K. J. and W. W. McMillian. 1967. Resistance in Corn to the Corn Earworm and Fall Armyworm. Part II: Types of Field Resistance to the Corn Earworm. J. Econ. Ent. 60:920–923.

Stevenson, F. J. and G. H. Wagner. 1970. Chemistry of Nitrogen in Soils. In *Agricultural Practices and Water Quality*. Iowa State University Press, Ames. pp. 125–141.

Stewart, B. A., F. G. Viets, G. L. Hutchinson and W. D. Kemper. 1967. Nitrate and Other Water Pollutants under Fields and Feedlots. Environ. Sci. Technol. 1:736.

Swanson, C. R. and W. C. Shaw. 1954. The effect of 2,4-dichlorophenoxyacetic acid on the hydrocyanic acid and nitrate content of Sudan grass. Agron. J. 46:418–421.

Tarrant, K. R., and J. O'G. Tatton. 1968. Organochlorine pesticides in rainwater in the British Isles. Nature 219:725–727.

Taylor, A. W., W. M. Edwards and E. C. Simpson. 1971. Nutrients in Streams Draining Woodland and Farmland near Coshocton, Ohio. Water Resource Research 7:81–89.

Teipel, J. W., G. M. Hass and R. L. Hill. 1968. The substrate specificity of fumarase. J. Biol. Chem. 243:5684–5693.

Terriere, L. C. 1968. Oxidation of pesticides, the comparative approach. In *Enzymatic Oxidation of Toxicants*, E. Hodgson (ed.). North Carolina State University, Raleigh.

Thorne, W. 1970. Agricultural Production in Irrigated Areas. In *Arid Lands in Transition*, Harold E. Dregne (ed). George W. King Printing Co., Baltimore, Md. pp. 31–56.

Tiedje, J. M. and M. Alexander. 1969. Enzymatic cleavage of the ether bond of 2,4-dichlorophenoxyacetate. J. Agric. Food Chem. 17:1080–1084.

Tiedje, J. M., J. M. Duxbury, M. Alexander and J. E. Dawson. 1969. 2,4-D metabolism: pathway of degradation of chlorocatechols by *Arthrobacter sp*. J. Agric. Food Chem. 17:1021–1026.

Todd, D. K. 1971. The Water Encyclopedia. Water Information Center. Port Washington, New York.

UN-FAO. 1963. Third World Food Survey. United Nations—Food and Agriculture Organization FFHC Basic Study No. 11. Rome.

UN-FAO. 1968. Forecast of export availabilities and import requirements of rice for 1968. United Nations–Food and Agriculture Organization, Study Group on Rice, Consultative Subcommittee on Economic Aspects of Rice. Rome.

UN-FAO. 1969. The effects of changes in the distribution of income upon projections of demand—preliminary report. United Nations–Food and Agriculture Organization, Commodities and Trade Div. Intersecretarial Expert Consultation on Projections. Rome.

U.S. Atomic Energy Commission. 1962. Civilian Nuclear Power–Report to the President.

U.S. Atomic Energy Commission. 1966. The Supplement to the 1962 Report to the President.

U.S. 86th Congress, 1st Session. 1960. Select Committee on National Water Resources. U.S. Senate, Committee Print No. 12, Land and Water Potentials and Future Requirements for Water. R. S. Kerr, Chairman.

U.S. 92nd Congress. 1971. Proceedings of the Joint Colloquium Before the Committee on Commerce. U.S. Senate; and the Committee on Science and Astronautics of the House of Representatives.

U.S. 92nd Congress, 1st Session. 1971. Comparative Committee Print. A Comparison of S.632 and S.992. U.S. Government Printing Office, Washington, D.C.

USDA. 1936. Agricultural Statistics, 1936. U.S. Government Printing Office, Washington, D.C. 421 pp.

USDA. 1954. *Losses in Agriculture.* Agricultural Research Service 20-1. U.S. Government Printing Office, Washington, D.C. 190 pp.

USDA. 1961. Agricultural Statistics, 1961. U.S. Government Printing Office, Washington, D.C. 624 pp.

USDA. 1964. Major Uses of Land and Water in the U.S. with Special Reference to Agriculture. ERS Agricultural Economic Rept. No. 149. U.S. Government Printing Office, Washington, D.C.

USDA. 1965. Agriculture Handbook No. 291. USDA Agricultural Research Service, Washington, D.C. 120 pp.

USDA. 1965a. Land Resource Regions and Major Land Resource Areas of the United States. Agriculture Handbook No. 296. USDA Soil Conservation Service, Washington, D.C.

USDA. 1968a. Extent of Farm Pesticide Use on Crops. Agricultural Economic Rept. No. 147. U.S. Government Printing Office, Washington, D.C.

USDA. 1968b. Handbook of Agricultural Charts-1968. Agriculture Handbook No. 359. United States Department of Agriculture, Washington, D.C.

USDA. 1968c. Major Uses of Land and Water in the U.S. with Special Reference to Agriculture Summary in 1964. Agricultural Economic Rept. No. 149. U.S. Government Printing Office, Washington, D.C.

USDA. 1968d. A National Program of Research for Environmental Quality. Pollution in Relation to Agriculture and Forestry. A report prepared by a joint task force of USDA and Directors of Agricultural Experiment Stations. USDA Research Program Development and Evaluation Staff, Washington, D.C.

USDA. 1969. Rural Indian Americans in Poverty. Agricultural Economic Rept. No. 167. U. S. Government Printing Office, Washington, D.C.

USDA. 1970a. Secretary of Agriculture's Report of 1969. United States Department of Agriculture, Washington, D.C.

USDA. 1970b. Rurality, Poverty and Health–Medical Problems in Rural Areas. Agricultural Economic Rept. No. 172. U.S. Government Printing Office, Washington, D.C.

USDA. 1970c. Guidelines for Research in Rural Development and Criteria to be Considered in the Selection of Centers of Excellence. CSRS-OD-1266. USDA Cooperative States Research Service, Washington, D.C.

USDA. 1970d. Agricultural Statistics, 1970. U.S. Government Printing Office, Washington, D.C. 627 pp.

USDA. 1970e. Quantities of Pesticides used by Farmers in 1966. Agricultural Economic Rept. No. 179. U.S. Government Printing Office, Washington, D.C.

USDA. 1970f. Progress Report on Rural Development. Office of Assistant Secretary, United States Department of Agriculture, Washington, D.C.

USDA. 1970g. Commercial Fertilizers, 1945-1969 Fiscal Years, Consumption of Commercial Fertilizer and Primary Plant Nutrients in the U.S. Annual Reports. 1970 Fiscal Year Preliminary Data. USDA Statistical Reporting Service, Washington, D.C.

USDA. 1971a. Environment: Using the Land. In *The Farm Index* 10(4):8-11.

USDA. 1971b. *Economic Research on Pesticides for Policy Decision-making.* Proceedings of a Symposium. U.S. Department of Agriculture, Washington, D.C.

USDA. 1971c. Exploring Our Cropland Potential. In *The Farm Index*, 10(9):11.

USDA. 1971d. The Pesticide Review 1970. USDA Agricultural Stabilization and Conservation Service, Washington, D.C. 32 pp.

USDA. 1971e. Animal Waste Reuse—Nutritive Value and Potential Problems from Feed Additives. A Review. USDA Agricultural Research Service, Washington, D.C. pp. 44-224.

USDA and the State Universities and Land Grant Colleges. 1968. A National Program of Research for Environmental Quality: Pollution in Relation to Agriculture and Forestry. Prepared by Joint Task Force. USDA Research Program Development and Evaluation Staff, Washington, D.C.

USDA and State Universities and Land Grant Colleges. 1969. A National Program of Research for Water and Watersheds. USDA Research Program Development and Evaluation Staff, Washington, D.C.

U.S. Department of HEW. 1969. Report of the Secretary's Commission on Pesticides and Their Relationship to Environmental Health. USDA Research Program Development and Evaluation Staff, Washington, D.C.

U.S. Department of the Interior. 1967. Outdoor Recreational Trends. United States Department of the Interior, Washington, D.C.

U.S. Department of the Interior. 1970. Mineral Facts and Problems. USDI Bureau of Mines Bull. No. 650. U.S. Government Printing Office, Washington, D.C.

U.S. Water Resources Council. 1967. United States Situation Paper, International Conference on Water for Peace. Washington, D.C.

U.S. Water Resources Council. 1968. *The Nation's Water Resources.* U.S. Government Printing Office, Washington, D.C.

U.S. Water Resources Council. 1969. Procedures for Evaluation of Water and Related Land Resource Projects. Report of Special Task Force. U.S. Government Printing Office, Washington, D.C.

U.S. Water Resources Council. 1970a. Principles for Planning Water and Land Resources. Report of Special Task Force. U.S. Government Printing Office, Washington, D.C.

U.S. Water Resources Council. 1970b. Standards for Planning Water and Land Resources. Report of Special Task Force. U.S. Goverment Printing Office, Wastington, D.C.

Van Gelder, G. A., W. B. Buck, R. Sandler, J. Maland, G. Karas and D. Elsberry. 1969. The effects of dieldrin and ruelene exposure on experimental behavior and electroencephalogram. In *The Biological Impact of Pesticides in the Environment.* Environmental Health Ser. 1, Oregon State University, Corvallis. pp. 125-133.

Verdun, J. 1970. Significance of Phosphates in Water Supplies. In *Agricultural Practices and Water Quality.* Iowa State University Press, Ames. pp. 63–71.

Viets, F. G., Jr. 1970. Soil Use and Water Quality—A Look into the Future. J. Agric. Food Chem. 18:789–792.

Wadleigh, C. A. 1968. Wastes in Relation to Agriculture and Forestry. USDA Misc. Publ. 1065. p. 112.

Wadleigh, C. A. and R. S. Dyal. 1970. Soils and Pollution. Agronomy and Health. American Society of Agronomy Special Publ. 16. Available: American Society of Agronomy, 677 S. Segue Road, Madison, Wisc. pp. 9–16.

Walker, W. H. 1969. Illinois Ground Water Pollution. J. Amer. Water Works Assn. 61:31.

Watt, K. E. 1964. The use of mathematics and computers to determine optimal strategy and tactics for a given pest control problem. Can. Ent. 96:202–249.

Webb, R. E. and F. Horsfall, Jr. 1967. Endrin resistance in the pine mouse. Science 156:1762.

Wedemeyer, G. 1967. Dechlorination of 1,1,1-trichloro-2,2-*bis*(p-chlorophenyl) ethane by *Aerobacter Aerogenes* 1. Metabolic products. Applied Microbial 15:569–574.

Weeks, L. G. 1960. The Next Hundred Years Energy Demand and Sources of Supply. Geo. Times 5(1). American Geological Institute, Washington, D.C.

Wegler, R. 1971. Problems and milestones in the development of a pesticide. An address given to an audience invited by Nihon Tokushu Noyaku Seizo K. K., in Yakugyo Kaikan, Tokyo.

Welch, L. F., F. A. Bazzoz, R. H. Harmeson, T. K. Hodges, B. A. Jones, Jr., F. J. Stevenson and R. L. Switzer. 1971. Plant Nutrients as Water Pollutants. Task Force Report in Proceedings of the *First Allerton Conference on Agriculture's Role in Environmental Quality.* University of Illinois, Urbana.

White, N. K. and D. K. Sunada. 1966. Ground Water Quality of Severence Basin, Weld County, Colorado. Civil Engineering Department, Colorado State University, Fort Collins.

White-Stevens, R. H. 1967. Producing protein for seven thousand million humans in the twenty-first century. Proceedings of the 7th International Congress of Nutrition, Hamburg, W. Germany. Problems of World Nutrition 4:925–935. Friedr. Vieweg and Sohn, Pergamon Press, Braunschweig.

Wiemeyer, S. N., and R. D. Porter. 1970. DDE thins eggshells of captive American kestrels. Nature, pp. 737–738.

Wiley, J. S. 1964. A Report on Three Manure Composting Plants. Compost Science 5:15–16 (Summer).

Windt, T. A., N. R. Bulley and L. M. Staley. 1971. Design, Installation and Biological Assessment of a Pasveer Oxidation Ditch on a Large British Columbia Swine Farm. In *Livestock Management and Pollution Abatement.* Proceedings of the International Symposium on Livestock Wastes. ASAE Publ. PROC-271. American Society of Agricultural Engineers, St. Joseph, Mich. pp. 213–216.

Witzel, S. A., N. E. Minshall, E. McCoy, R. J. Olson and K. T. Crabtree. 1969. The Effect of Farm Wastes on the Pollution of Natural Waters. Paper 69-428, presented at the Annual Meeting, American Society of Agricultural Engineers, Lafayette, Ind.

Wollman, H., and G. W. Bonem. 1971. The Outlook for Water, Quality, Quantity and National Growth. Published for Resources for the Future, Inc., by The Johns Hopkins Press, Baltimore, Md.

References

Wolman, A. 1962. Water Resources: A Report of the Committee on Natural Resources. NAS-NRC Publ. No. 100-B. National Academy of Sciences, Washington, D.C.

Wu, T. T., E. C. C. Lin and S. Tanaka. 1968. Mutants of *Aerobacter aerogenes* capable of utilizing xylitol as a novel carbon source. J. Bact. 96:447–456.

Yates, M. L., W. Holswade and A. I. Higer. 1970. Pesticide residues in hydrobiological environments. 159th ACS National Meeting, Houston, Tex. Water, Air and Waste Chemistry Section of the American Chemical Society Abstract, p. Watr-032.

Yushok, W. and F. E. Bear. 1948. Poultry Manure—Its Preservation, Deodorization and Disinfection. New Jersey Agr. Exp. Sta. Bull. No. 707. Rutgers University, New Brunswick, N.J.

Bibliography

Advisory Commission on Intergovernmental Relations. 1968. *Urban and Rural America: Policies for Future Growth.* U.S. Government Printing Office, Washington, D.C.

American Chemical Society. 1969. Pesticides in the Environment. In *Cleaning our Environment: The Chemical Basis for Action.* American Chemical Society, Washington, D.C. pp. 195–244.

American Society of Agricultural Engineers. 1966. *Management of Farm Animal Wastes.* Proceedings, National Symposium on Animal Waste Management. ASAE Publ. No. SP-0366. American Society of Agricultural Engineers, St. Joseph, Mich.

American Society of Agricultural Engineers. 1971. *Livestock Waste Management and Pollution Abatement.* Proceedings, International Symposium on Livestock Wastes. ASAE Publ. PROC-271. American Society of Agricultural Engineers, St. Joseph, Mich.

Anon. 1969. *Animal Waste Management.* Cornell Conference on Agricultural Waste Management. Syracuse, N.Y.

Anon. 1970. *Relationship of Agriculture to Soil and Water Pollution.* Cornell Conference on Agricultural Waste Management. Rochester, N.Y. 270 p.

Anon. 1971. *Agricultural Wastes–Principles and Guidelines for Practical Solutions.* Cornell Conference on Agricultural Waste Management. Syracuse, N.Y.

Brady, N. C. (ed.) 1967. *Agriculture and the Quality of Our Environment.* AAAS Publ. 85. Washington, D.C. 460 p.

Borlaug, N. E. 1972. Mankind and Civilization at Another Crossroad. In Balance with Nature–A Biological Myth. Bio. Science 22:1. pp. 41–44.

Clawson, M. and J. L. Knetsch. 1966. *Economics of Outdoor Recreation.* Resources for the Future, Inc., Washington, D.C.

187

Doxiadis, A. 1970. Ekistics, the Science of Human Settlements. Science 170:3956. pp. 393–404.

Entomological Society of Canada. 1970. Pesticides and the Environment. Supplement to Bull. Entomol. Soc. Can. 3:1. 14 pp.

Freeman, O. F., and I. L. Bennett, Jr. 1969. *Control of Agriculture-Related Pollution.* A Report to the President. Office of Science and Technology and USDA. 102 p.

Frink, C. R. 1969. Water Pollution Potential Estimated from Farm Nutrient Budgets. Agron. J. 61:550–553.

Goldstein, J. H. 1971. *Competition for Wetlands in the Midwest. An economic analysis.* Resources for the Future, Inc., Washington, D.C.

Hanson, A. A. 1972. A Directed Ecosystem Approach to Pest Control and Environmental Quality. J. Environ. Quality 1:45–54.

Heady, E. O., H. C. Madsen, K. J. Nicol and S. H. Hargrove. 1971. *Future Water and Land Use: Effects of Selected Public Agricultural and Irrigation Policies on Water Demand and Use.* A report of the Center for Agricultural and Rural Development, Iowa State University, Ames, prepared for the National Water Commission. National Technical Information Service, Springfield, Va. PB 206-790 (NWC-EES-71-003).

Heady, E. O., H. C. Madsen, K. J. Nicol and S. H. Hargrove. 1972. Agricultural and Water Policies and the Environment. CARD Rept. No. 40T. Center for Agricultural and Rural Development, Iowa State University, Ames.

Joint Task Force of Southern Agricultural Experiment Station Directors and USDA. 1970. *Environmental Quality—Pollution in Relation to Agriculture and Forestry.* U.S. Department of Agriculture, Washington, D.C. 37 p.

Joint Task Force of USDA and State Universities and Land Grant Colleges. 1968. *A National Program of Research for Environmental Quality-Pollution in Relation to Agriculture and Forestry.* U.S. Department of Agriculture, Washington, D.C. 111 p.

Jones, D. D., and D. L. Day and A. C. Dale. 1970. Aerobic Treatment of Livestock Wastes. Illinois Agr. Exp. Sta. Bull. No. 737. 55 pp.

Knipling, E. F. 1972. Use of Organisms to Control Insect Pests. J. Environ. Quality 1:34–40.

Landsberg, H. 1964. *Natural Resources for U.S. Growth—A Look Ahead to the Year 2000.* The Johns Hopkins Press, Baltimore, Md.

Loehr, R. C. 1968. *Pollution Implications of Animal Wastes: A Forward Oriented Review.* Federal Water Pollution Control Administration, U.S. Department of the Interior, Washington, D. C. 175 pp.

Loehr, R. C. 1970. Changing Practices in Agriculture and Their Effect on the Environment. In *Critical Reviews in Environmental Control.* Chemical Rubber Co., Cleveland, Ohio.

Loehr, R. C. 1971. Alternatives for the Treatment and Disposal of Animal Wastes. J. Water Pollution Control Federation 43:668–678.

Loehr, R. C. 1972. Animal Waste Management—Problems and Guidelines for Solutions. J. Environ. Quality 1:71–78.

Miner, J. R. (ed.) 1971. Farm Animal-Waste Management. (North Central Regional Research Publication 206) Iowa Agr. Exp. Sta. Spec. Rep. 67. 44 pp.

Morrison, W. E. and C. L. Readling. 1968. An Energy Model for the U.S. USDI Bureau of Mines Info. Cir. No. 8384.

Muehling, A. J. 1969. Swine Housing and Waste Management—A Research Review. Publ. AEng-873. Department of Agricultural Engineering, University of Illinois, Urbana. 91 pp.

National Academy of Sciences. 1968. *Water and Choice in the Colorado Basin.* Report of the Committee on Water. NAS-NRC Publ. 1689. National Academy of Sciences, Washington, D.C. 107 pp.

National Academy of Sciences. 1968. *Weed Control.* Vol. 2 of the series: Principles of Plant and Animal Pest Control. NAS-NRC Publ. 1597. National Academy of Sciences, Washington, D.C. 471 pp.

National Academy of Sciences. 1969. *Insect Pest Management and Control.* Vol. 3 of the series: Principles of Plant and Animal Pest Control. NAS-NRC Publ. 1696. National Academy of Sciences, Washington, D.C. 508 pp.

National Academy of Sciences. 1969. *Eutrophication: Causes, Consequences, Correctives.* Proceedings of a Symposium. National Academy of Sciences, Washington, D.C. 661 pp.

Nelson, L. B. 1972. Agricultural Chemicals in Relation to Environmental Quality: Chemical Fertilizers, Present and Future. J. Environ. Quality 1:2–6.

President's National Advisory Commission on Rural Poverty. 1968. *Rural Poverty in the United States.* U.S. Government Printing Office, Washington, D.C.

Snoeyink, V. and Virginia Griffin (eds.). 1970. *Nitrates and Water Supply: Source and Control.* Proceedings, 12th Sanitary Engineering Conference. Department of Civil Engineering, University of Illinois, Urbana.

Stanford, G., C. B. England and A. W. Taylor. 1970. Fertilizer Use and Water Quality. USDA-ARS Publication 41-168.

U.S. Dept. of Agriculture. 1971. *Economic Research on Pesticides for Policy Decision-making.* Proceedings of a Symposium. U.S. Department of Agriculture, Washington, D.C.

U.S. Dept. of Health, Education, and Welfare. 1969. *Report of the Secretary's Commission on Pesticides and Their Relationship to Environmental Health.* U.S. Government Printing Office, Washington, D.C. 677 pp.

U.S. Dept. of the Interior. 1970. Mineral Facts and Problems. USDI Bureau of Mines Bull. No. 650.

U.S. Water Resources Council. 1968. *The Nation's Water Resources.* U.S. Government Printing Office, Washington, D.C.

Viets, F. G., Jr. 1970. Soil Use and Water Quality—A Look into the Future. J. Agr. Food Chem. 18:789–792.

Wadleigh, C. H. 1968. Wastes in Relation to Agriculture and Forestry. USDA Misc. Publ. 1065. U.S. Government Printing Office, Washington, D.C. 112 p.

Willrich, T. L., and G. E. Smith (eds.) 1970. *Agricultural Practices and Water Quality.* Iowa State University, Ames. 415 p.

Wollman, H., and G. W. Bonem. 1971. *The Outlook for Water, Quality, Quantity and National Growth.* Published for Resources for the Future, Inc., by The Johns Hopkins Press, Baltimore, Md.

ISBN 0-309-02215-0